Challenging behaviour
and people with learning disabilities
A handbook

Edited by Steve Hardy and Theresa Joyce

Contents

Introduction

Steve Hardy and Theresa Joyce

People with learning disabilities who have behaviour that is described as challenging are one of the most vulnerable groups in society. They are at risk of being excluded from services, being denied opportunities and being placed away from their local communities and families. Furthermore, they are vulnerable to poor practice and abuse.

This handbook is timely, and essential to help ensure that there is a competent workforce that has the capabilities to provide effective, ethical and high-quality support to people whose behaviour is described as challenging. When developing this handbook we have made every effort to adhere to the Charter that has been developed by the Challenging Behaviour – National Strategy Group. The following rights and values are at the centre of the charter:

- People will be supported to exercise their human rights (which are the same as everyone else's) to be healthy, full and valued members of their community with respect for their culture, ethnic origin, religion, age, gender, sexuality and disability.
- All children who are at risk of presenting behavioural challenges have the right to have their needs identified at an early stage, leading to co-ordinated early intervention and support.
- All families have the right to be supported to maintain the physical and emotional well-being of the family unit.
- All individuals have the right to receive person-centred support and services that are developed on the basis of a detailed understanding of their support needs, including their communication needs. This will be individually tailored, flexible, responsive to changes in individual circumstances, and delivered in the most appropriate local situation.
- People have the right to a healthy life, and be given the appropriate support to achieve this.
- People have the same rights as everyone else to a family and social life, relationships, housing, education, employment and leisure.

- People have the right to support and services that create capable environments for individuals, which are developed on the principles of positive behavioural support and other evidence-based approaches and which draw from additional specialist input as needed. This will respond to all the needs of the individual.
- People have the right not to be hurt or damaged or humiliated in any way by interventions. Support and services must strive to achieve this.
- People have the right to receive support and care based on good and up-to-date evidence.

(The Challenging Behaviour Foundation – www.thecbf.org.uk)

The clinical content of this handbook is firmly based on the best practice as laid out in *Challenging Behaviour: A unified approach* (RCPsych *et al,* 2007). Our approach is based on that of positive behavioural support, offering person-centred support, individualised interventions that are clearly based on a functional assessment, understanding the person's needs and the environment in which they live. Chapters are included that address assessment and a range of interventions, such as communication, reactive strategies, active support and skills teaching. In addition to good practice, we have included chapters that address other important issues such as autism and legal frameworks.

This handbook is aimed at frontline staff in health and social care settings who support people with behaviour described as challenging on a regular basis. However, professionals who are undergoing training are also likely to find the handbook useful.

Improving the lives of people whose behaviour is described as challenging is everybody's business and there is a multitude of stakeholders involved. The inclusion of families and people with learning disabilities is key and in the handbook there are chapters that give the perspectives of these two important groups.

We have endeavoured make this handbook as user-friendly and as accessible as possible. We very much hope that you find it a valuable resource in helping to improve the lives of people with behaviour described as challenging.

We would like to thank all the authors who have contributed to this handbook.

Contributors

Saadia Arshad MBBS MRCPsych
Specialist registrar
Psychiatry of Learning Disability, South London and Maudsley NHS Foundation Trust

Saadia works for people with learning disabilities who have ongoing mental health needs. Her specialist interests include epilepsy and autism. She is currently pursuing a masters degree in epilepsy at King's College, London. She has published articles in peer-reviewed journals.

Peter Baker
Consultant clinical psychologist
Challenging Needs Service, Sussex Partnership NHS Foundation Trust, Gambier House, West Hill Rd, St Leonards on Sea, East Sussex

Dr Peter Baker is a consultant clinical psychologist for Sussex Partnership NHS Foundation Trust and an honorary senior lecturer at the Tizard Centre, University of Kent. His clinical work in Sussex includes leadership responsibilities for the trust's three specialist adult challenging behaviour services based in Brighton, Hastings and Worthing. He lectures at the Tizard Centre on the certificate, diploma, graduate and masters programmes and is widely published in the area of challenging behaviour and learning disability.

Jill Bradshaw
Lecturer in learning disability (honorary)
Tizard Centre, University of Kent, Canterbury, Kent, CT2 7LZ

After training as a speech and language therapist, Jill worked with adults with learning disabilities and challenging behaviour. As her interest in research developed, she went to work at the Tizard Centre as a lecturer in learning disabilities. Jill contributed to the centre's teaching, research and consultancy work. She has published work on staff communication, communication and challenging behaviour, active support and training staff to work with people with challenging behaviour. She completed her PhD in attributions of challenging behaviour and views of communication at Manchester Metropolitan University in 2008. She has an honorary post as lecturer at the Tizard Centre.

Mark Burns
Consultant clinical psychologist and intensive support team manager
Intensive Support Team, The Ridge Hill Centre, Brierley Hill Road, Stourbridge, West Midlands, DY8 5ST

Mark is a consultant clinical psychologist who co-ordinates the specialist assessment and intervention to people whose behaviour is described as severely challenging in Dudley. His interests include cognitive behaviour therapy and staff training and support.

Alick Bush
Consultant clinical psychologist
Psychology Services, St George's Community Health Centre, Winter Street, Sheffield, S3 7ND

Dr Alick Bush is a consultant clinical psychologist and clinical director in the Sheffield Joint Learning Disabilities Service. He is also an honorary teacher at Sheffield University. Alick has extensive experience of working with adults with learning disabilities whose behaviour challenges services. His clinical work involves helping care support teams to understand why a behaviour might be occurring and how a person can be supported in ways that make it less likely that they will need to show behaviours that carers find challenging. Alick set up and managed a community-based intensive support service for people who challenge services, and is currently involved in the development of local services for this group of service users.

He has served as chair and policy lead for the British Psychological Society Faculty of Learning Disabilities, and co-authored the *BPS Clinical Practice Guidelines: Psychological interventions for severely challenging behaviours shown by people with learning disabilities* (BPS, 2004). He also co-authored the joint professions report *Challenging Behaviour: A unified approach. Clinical and service guidelines for supporting people with learning disabilities who are at risk of receiving abusive or restrictive practices* (RCPsych, BPS, RCS<, 2007).

Peter Carpenter

Consultant psychiatrist in learning disabilities.
Avon and Wiltshire Mental Health Partnership NHS Trust, Kingswood Learning Disability Service, Hanham Road, Bristol, BS15 8PQ

After his initial training in Leicester, Dr Peter Carpenter did further training in Bristol where he is now a consultant and associate medical lead for Avon & Wiltshire Partnership Mental Health Partnership NHS Trust. Peter has been working with children and adults with autism spectrum conditions for over 20 years. Currently an honorary clinical lecturer at the University of Bristol, he is also involved in the current regional developments for adults with Aspergers' syndrome in the southwest and the NICE guideline development group for adults. He has written on autism, service development and the history of learning disability psychiatry and teaches widely on these subjects.

Eddie Chaplin

Research and strategy lead
Estia Centre, 66 Snowsfield, London, SE1 3SS

Eddie is the research and strategy lead for the Behavioural and Developmental Psychiatry Clinical Academic Group of the South London and Maudsley NHS Foundation Trust. He has extensive clinical experience in national learning disability and neurodevelopmetal services. Eddie helped to develop and teaches on a number of academic courses at the Institute of Psychiatry. He is also involved in a variety of research projects involving people with learning disabilities, which include guided self-help, substance abuse and prison pathways.

Viv Cooper

Chair of trustees
The Challenging Behaviour Foundation, The Old Courthouse, New Road Avenue, Chatham, Kent, ME4 6BE

Viv has three children and her eldest son, Daniel, has severe learning disabilities and behaviour described as challenging. When Daniel was nine he had to leave home to go to a specialist residential school, which was 275 miles away from his family, because there was no local provision that could meet his needs. Daniel has now moved back to his local area and lives in his own house with his own staff support team.

In 1997 Viv founded the charity, the Challenging Behaviour Foundation (CBF). CBF is a small, national charity that provides a range of information and support to families of children and adults who have severe learning disabilities and behaviour described as challenging. In addition to developing family-friendly, practical information and resources, the CBF works strategically to deliver change and has established a Challenging Behaviour National Strategy Group, made up of senior stakeholders, which has agreed a charter to improve support and services. Viv worked part-time for the Valuing People Now team, working jointly with Cally Ward leading on the family work programme. Through this work the National Valuing Families Forum was developed to ensure that 'grassroots' experiences are fed up to government.

Peter Cronin
Service user consultant
Estia Centre, 66 Snowsfield, London SE1 3SS

Peter is a service user consultant and trainer at the Estia Centre. He has published several articles and teaches support staff on various topics. He is also an MP for the People's Parliament in the London Borough of Lewisham.

Shoumitro Deb, MBBS, MD, FRCPsych,
Consultant neuropsychiatrist
University of Birmingham, The Barberry, 25 Vincent Drive, Birmingham, B15 2FG

Professor Shoumitro Deb is a consultant in neuropsychiatry of adult learning disabilities and acquired brain injury. He has contributed to over 150 publications including the Royal College of Psychiatrists' publication on the management of imminent violence in learning disability. Shoumitro has been involved in developing national and international guides on the psychotropic use of medications in learning disabilities and the first European guide on the assessment and diagnosis of mental disorders in learning disabilities. He is a programme director for psychiatry, neuropsychiatry and epilepsy MSc courses and co-chair of the World Psychiatric Association LD-Section. Shoumitro is a member of various training and education committees and has been a MRCPsych/CASC examiner for over 12 years. He is the training programme director in the West Midlands and a working group member for the WHO ICD-11-ID.

Jo Dwyer
Clinical specialist occupational therapist
Lewisham Team for Adults with Learning Disabilities, 19–21 Brownhill Road, London, SE6 2HG

Since qualifying as an occupational therapist in 1997, Jo has spent the majority of her career working with adults with learning disabilities. She completed an MSc in occupational therapy in 2007, focusing on various aspects of the occupational therapy role with people with learning disabilities. Jo has presented both nationally and internationally and has published work pertaining to her role. She has been a member of various national committees and working parties considering issues facing people with learning disabilities. Jo currently works clinically in a community learning disabilities team with some input into an inpatient assessment and treatment facility. Her clinical interests include working with people with additional mental health issues or with behaviours described as challenging.

Ian Hall
Consultant psychiatrist
Community Learning Disability Service, Beaumont House, Mile End Hospital, Bancroft Road, London, E1 4DG

Dr Ian Hall is a consultant psychiatrist for people with learning disabilities in East London and an honorary senior lecturer in psychiatry of learning disability at Queen Mary, University of London. He is chair of the Faculty of Psychiatry of Learning Disability at the Royal College of Psychiatrists, and has worked with them on their policy in relation to mental health law and autism. He is interested in developing innovative service models for people with learning disabilities who have mental health problems and/or challenging behaviour, and is particularly interested in incorporating user and carer views into service development.

Sarah Halls
Training and development co-ordinator
Estia Centre, 66 Snowsfield, London, SE1 3SS

Sarah is the training and development co-ordinator at the Estia Centre. She graduated in 2002 with a BSc (Hons) in Psychology. Sarah has worked in outreach, residential and day services for people with learning disabilities and mental health problems. She has also worked as an assistant psychologist, helping to develop and run a specialist assessment and treatment unit for people with learning disabilities and severely challenging behaviour. She has published books and training materials, as well as articles for the journal *Advances in Mental Health and Intellectual Disabilities*.

Steve Hardy
Training and consultancy manager
Estia Centre, Munro Centre – Guy's Hospital, 66 Snowsfield, London, SE1 3SS

Steve Hardy is the training and consultancy manager at the Estia Centre, South London and Maudsley NHS Foundation Trust. He has worked in mental health and challenging behaviour services for people with learning disabilities for 20 years and has widely published in these areas. He is also the co-editor of the journal Advances in Mental Health and Learning Disabilities.

Jayne Henry
Clinical psychologist
Eric Shepherd Unit, Woodside Rd, Abbots Langley, Hertfordshire, WD5 0HT

Dr Jane Henry works as a clinical psychologist with offenders with learning disabilities in both medium and low secure services at the Eric Shepherd Forensic Services, HPFT. She is involved in running and delivering the sex offender treatment programme and is involved in a range of individual and group treatment programmes, with a particular interest in offenders with personality disorder. Jane also teaches at the Institute of Psychiatry and University of Hertfordshire on the doctorate courses for clinical psychology.

Cleia Hayashi
Lead clinician occupational therapist
Lewisham Teams for Adults with Learning Disabilities, 19–21 Brownhill Road, London, SE6 2HG.

Cleia is the clinical lead occupational therapist working across Lewisham and Southwark Community Teams for Adults with Learning Disabilities. Originally from Brazil, she graduated from university with a BA in OT in 1980, and following this she worked in various settings including acute hospitals, private clinics and lectured on an OT degree course. Since coming to Britain in 1989 she has primarily worked in learning disability services. Apart from having clinical and managerial responsibility for the

OT team across two boroughs, she is strategic lead for the development of multidisciplinary clinical pathway for people with Down's syndrome and dementia.

Theresa Joyce
Consultant Clinical Psychologist
South London and Maudsley NHS Foundation Trust

Theresa Joyce is a consultant clinical psychologist and leads on the Mental Capacity Act (2005) and safeguarding adults for the South London and Maudsley NHS Foundation Trust. Theresa has extensive experience in developing and managing specialist services for people with learning disabilities whose behaviour is described as challenging. She is one of the authors of *Challenging Behaviour: A unified approach*, which are the clinical and service guidelines published by the Royal College of Psychiatrists, British Psychological Society and the Royal College of Speech and Language Therapists.

Stephen C. Oathamshaw
Consultant clinical psychologist/head of specialty
Scottish Borders Learning Disability Service, West Grove Annexe, Waverley Road, Melrose, TD6 9SL

Dr Stephen Oathamshaw is consultant clinical psychologist for the Scottish Borders Learning Disability Service and head of specialty. He is employed by NHS Borders. Stephen has worked in learning disability services since 1988, working in day service and residential services with people who challenged services and qualifying as a learning disability nurse in 1993. Stephen worked in community challenging needs teams for six years in South London and was also employed as a lecturer in learning disability nursing for one year.

Stephen moved to northwest England in 2001 and qualified as a clinical psychologist on the Manchester clinical psychology doctorate training course in 2004. During his psychology training he developed an interest in the application and modification of cognitive behavioural therapy (CBT) to the treatment of psychological difficulties in people who have learning disabilities. He has continued this interest through clinical work, research, conference presentations, teaching and publication since qualifying and also has particular interests in the application of modified CBT to the treatment of psychosis and anger problems in people who have learning disabilities.

Stephen moved to become head of specialty for the psychology service for people with learning disabilities in the Scottish Borders in 2009.

Anne Parris
Senior behavioural support practitioner
Lambeth Learning Disabilities Partnership, Phoenix House, 10 Wandsworth Road, London, SW8 2LL

Anne has worked with people with learning disabilities whose behaviour has been described as challenging for 15 years. Her first job was as a support worker in a large residential service in the northwest, before working for the NHS in a small residential service in Kent. She has worked as a behavioural support practitioner since 2000. Anne completed the diploma in applied psychology in learning disabilities (challenging behaviour) at the Tizard Centre, University of Kent, in 2004. She is currently a senior behavioural support practitioner offering specialist assessment and intervention.

John Rose
Academic director
Department of clinical psychology, University of Birmingham, Edgbaston, Birmingham, B15 2TT

John is academic director of the clinical psychology training course at the University of Birmingham and works in the Psychological Health Service in Dudley. Prior to this he worked on the Cardiff clinical psychology training course and as a clinical psychologist in a number of different clinical services. He has written over 100 articles in academic and professional journals on issues related to cognitive therapy, service design, offenders with intellectual disabilities and staff and organisational issues in intellectual disability services. He continues to apply his academic interests in practice. He continues to develop his interest in staff support and organisational issues. He is also currently collaborating with colleagues on a major trial of anger management for people with intellectual disabilities where direct care staff are being supported to deliver therapy directly. He is also involved in research investigating the training needs of staff who work with people who have intellectual disabilities and mental health issues.

Lisa Russell
Behaviour specialist
Southwark Learning Disability Team, Mabel Goldwin House, 49 Grange Walk, London, SE1P 5LX

As a behaviour specialist, Lisa's role is to provide assessment and interventions for people with learning disabilities who have complex challenging behaviours. Lisa graduated from the Tizard Centre, University of Kent (UK). The aim of Lisa's work is to promote the highest standards of care and support, working with one of the most vulnerable populations in society, using non-aversive, person-centred behavioural techniques. She has helped to develop and deliver training for staff and families for the Estia Centre (South London and Maudsley Foundation NHS Trust, part of King's Health Partners, London) and has had work published as part of this role.

John Shephard
Behaviour specialist
Sussex Partnership NHS Foundation Trust, Gambier House, West Hill Road, St Leonards on Sea, East Sussex, TN38 0NG

John has worked in learning disability services as practitioner, service manager, trainer and consultant for more than 20 years. Since 1990 his work has primarily been concerned with people who exhibit severe challenging behaviour. He is currently working as a behaviour specialist with Sussex Partnership NHS Foundation Trust. His particular interests are environmental factors in the causes and management of challenging behaviour, the development of non-aversive interventions, and the promotion of positive behavioural support.

Amanda Sinai
Higher trainee
Community Learning Disability Service, Beaumont House, Mile End Hospital, Bancroft Road, London, E1 4DG

Dr Amanda Sinai is a higher trainee in learning disability psychiatry on the North London Learning Disability Rotation. Her particular interests are behavioural phenotypes and medical education.

Karen Watson
Occupational therapy clinical specialist
Lambeth Learning Disability Partnership, 7th Floor, Phoenix House,
10 Wandsworth Road, Vauxhall, London, SW8 2LL

After her psychology degree, Karen went onto to qualify as an occupational therapist in 1994. With over 15 years' experience working in the field of learning disabilities, she is currently the clinical specialist occupational therapist for Lambeth learning disabilities team. Her practice is based on empowerment and collaboration with the people who use services and their carers. She has a keen interest in imparting her knowledge and skills to facilitate the learning and development of others.

Peter Woodward RNLD, MSc, PGDipHE, DipA.Psychol., DipN.
Senior lecturer in learning disabilities
University of Greenwich, Avery Hill Campus, Southwood site, 101 Mary Seacole, Avery Hill Road, London, SE9 2UG

Peter has worked with people with learning disabilities since 1993. He qualified as a learning disability nurse working in challenging behaviour, mental health and forensic settings before entering education. He is senior lecturer in learning disabilities at the University of Greenwich and is currently conducting research into mental health in learning disabilities.

Chapter 1

Challenging behaviour

Peter Woodward

People with learning disabilities often engage in behaviour that we consider to be a challenge. In the past this behaviour was given labels such as 'problem behaviour'. These labels and terms were not helpful as they imply that the person is being a problem or is difficult. If we think of behaviour being challenging we should not be thinking about an individual that we are having trouble with, but instead about how we need to rise to the challenge of supporting them appropriately. It is a challenge for us as carers to give individuals the right level of support. It is also worth noting that it is not the person that is challenging, but their behaviour. When we start to think of individuals as being challenging rather than their behaviour, we are again returning to the idea that they are a problem. The first part of the challenge is to look at what we can change in the person's environment that will help make the behaviour less likely to happen.

Defining challenging behaviour

It is useful to have a definition of challenging behaviour for reference. One of the best known and most widely used definitions in the UK is by Eric Emerson.

'Culturally abnormal behaviour(s) of such intensity, frequency or duration that the physical safety of the person or others is likely to be placed in serious jeopardy, or behaviour which is likely to seriously limit use of, or result in the person being denied access to, ordinary community services.'
(Emerson, 1995)

To understand the definition more clearly, it can be helpful to break it down and look at its components individually.

'Culturally abnormal behaviour(s)': This means behaviours that are not normal for the situation you are in. It may be normal for us to behave a certain way in one situation, but not acceptable for us to behave that way in a different situation. For example, it is normal to strip almost naked on the beach in summer but this would not be normal behaviour on a high street in winter. It is normal to throw punches and kicks when training for a black belt in karate, but not at the theatre. It is normal to scream and shout when your horse approaches the finishing line at the Grand National, but not during a wedding. Screaming, stripping and punching may or may not be challenging behaviours depending on the environment.

'Safety of self or others being placed in serious jeopardy': Is anyone in danger? This means people in danger of being physically hurt and the danger of someone harming themself. Danger can also be emotional.

'Likely to seriously limit use of, or ... being denied access to, ordinary community services': Will the behaviour stop the person from going out; will it stop them from going to the places that everyone should have a right to go to? This could be the library, swimming baths, hairdressers, cub scouts, football stadium etc. Here we have to think about how someone's behaviour can limit their quality of life. Screaming loudly will probably not do a great deal of harm to anyone in the long run but it would probably stop someone from being welcome in a restaurant.

Case study: Sam

Sam has severe learning disabilities and mobility problems. He wakes up at 6am but cannot get out of bed without the support of staff who start work at 7am. When staff arrive they also support the other four people who Sam lives with. Three of Sam's housemates attend a day centre in the mornings and are supported to wash, dress and eat breakfast before Sam so that the bus can pick them up at 9am. Sam is eventually supported to wash and dress and is then taken to the lounge while his breakfast is prepared. Sam has now been awake for several hours and has not eaten.

Sam attends the day centre on different days to his housemates and when he sees the people he lives with being assisted to board the bus, he cannot understand why he is not going with them. Sam is also hungry and can see the breakfast plates of the others on the table. He begins to shout and slap his head violently. The stressed staff, who are rushing to meet the bus, see Sam and feel that he should not go out that day 'because his behaviour is out of control'.

In this example, the challenge would be for the staff to look at how they allocate and distribute their time, and how they let Sam know what is going on. Sam's behaviour is not a problem – it is understandable given the circumstances.

If we examine the example of Sam, we can see that his behaviour could be described as challenging. Sam's behaviour is not 'culturally normal'; most people do not scream and hit themselves. When we view his behaviour objectively, it is understandable given the circumstances but it is usually not normal. Sam's own 'safety was being placed in jeopardy'; if someone continuously hits themself they are likely to cause bruising, swelling and in the long-run, disfigurement and permanent damage. Sam's behaviour was 'likely to limit his use of community services' in that staff felt they could not take someone who was screaming and self-injuring out that day.

It is worth noting that stopping Sam from going out is likely to limit his life further and probably make challenging behaviour even more likely to happen. Instead, the staff team need to find out why the behaviour is happening and work in a different way so that it does not happen in future. This will be a challenge for them but, as stated earlier, this is why it is called challenging behaviour. We also need to consider the idea that challenging behaviour happens for a reason. When we go to work, chat with friends, avoid traffic during rush hour, or take a long soak in the bath, we are doing this for a reason. We do not randomly and suddenly start showing odd behaviours for no reason.

Why challenging behaviour happens

There are five possible reasons why behaviour we find a challenge could be happening. It could be because the person needs **attention** from somebody, because they want to **escape** from an unpleasant situation, for **sensory stimulation**, to gain access to a **tangible** object or because they are in some form of physical or mental distress – they have an **illness**. Each factor is discussed below.

- **Attention:** The need to have social attention from others. You may hear staff saying that someone is 'attention seeking' and using the term in a pejorative way. However, the vast majority of us seek attention from our friends, loved ones and even complete strangers. This behaviour might be shown by someone with a learning disability taking their clothes off because they have learned that when this happens staff come over and get them dressed again.
- **Escape:** This is the need to get away from something. The reasons why might be due to not understanding what is happening and so wanting to escape, or having learned that something causes discomfort. An example could be someone with learning disabilities who is given vacuum cleaning to do as a household chore. They may find that the vacuum cleaner is noisy, difficult to manoeuvre and that it collides with objects. When the task becomes too much for them they start to wave the hose around threateningly. A member of staff then quickly switches it off and the task stops. A job like vacuum cleaning may be difficult for someone to understand, but a task like making a sandwich might make more sense because the individual can see the whole process, understand why they are doing it, and get a sandwich at the end of it.
- **Sensory stimulation:** This is the attempt to stimulate ourselves – to provide our senses with something interesting. For example, someone with a learning disability may pull their hair out for the sensation it gives them; they may hum or sing out continuously; they may prod at their eyelids to see the colours that this act produces. Sensory stimulation is more likely to happen when people are left unoccupied or unstimulated for long periods of time.

- **Tangible:** This is where the person gains something due to their behaviour. This could be a preferred item such as a toy, video game, magazine, or food and drink. For example, a member of staff hears one of the people she is supporting start to shout and swear; they know from experience that a drink will often distract the person and so bring him a cup of tea. The man receiving the drink has learned that if he shouts and swears he sometimes gets given a cup of tea (the tangible object).
- **Illness:** The fifth reason why some challenging behaviours might happen is due to illness. For example, a man with severe learning disabilities might punch himself in the cheek due to toothache, frequently jab a finger into a painful ear, or scratch repeatedly at an itchy scab. However, the majority of challenging behaviour is caused by what is happening in the person's environment and for the reasons already listed. Illness may be something that makes escape, attention, getting something tangible, or self-stimulation more likely. An example might be having a headache, which could make someone feel the need for the attention of others more. Feeling depressed might make a person want to be on their own and when a member of staff constantly tries to get them to do their favourite activity, they may lash out to escape. It can be seen that the underlying illness, such as a headache, is increasing the need for attention, or depression is increasing the need for escape. It is not helpful to think that all challenging behaviour is caused by an underlying illness or a mental health problem, as it is usually caused by something in the person's environment. Regular reviewing of an individual's health should be something to consider when thinking about challenging behaviour.

We can apply these reasons to our own behaviour (as noted above). We go to work (to receive a tangible – our wages), we chat to friends (because we like their attention), we avoid traffic jams (to escape) and we take long soaks in the bath (for sensory stimulation).

Reacting appropriately to challenging behaviour

The final thing to consider is how we react to challenging behaviour. Many of us have learned that 'bad' behaviour results in punishment; this may be because we recall situations in our childhood when we were punished for behaving in a 'bad' or 'naughty' manner. This experience may be the only reference we have in dealing with behaviour that is challenging and we may revert back to thinking that punishment will work. However, punishment is not an effective way of reducing behaviour that we find a challenge. If punishment was effective you would have been sent to your room or scolded as a three year old and never been 'naughty' again. It is also highly likely that the forty-year-old man with learning disabilities who you support whose behaviour is described as challenging has been punished hundreds of times throughout his life and yet, here we are, forty years later, and his behaviour is still challenging.

When working with people whose behaviour is a challenge we need to look at what is going on in their environment (the way we interact, the layout of the house, the routines) that may make certain behaviours more or less likely to occur. We need to try to teach new skills so that the people we support can cope better in certain situations. We also need to encourage new behaviours so that challenging behaviour is not a preferred option and, finally, we need to know how to respond when we see challenging behaviour in a way that is not punishing.

In Sam's case, his supporters need to examine what is going on in his environment that causes him to scream and slap himself. They need to find out why it is happening: is it to escape, for attention, stimulation or to gain something tangible? His supporters need to change the way they work with Sam to make the behaviour less likely to happen and to teach him new and appropriate behaviours. They also need to react in a way that is not punishing and does not limit his quality of life any further.

Conclusion

- It is called challenging behaviour because it is a challenge to us to find appropriate ways of supporting people.
- Challenging behaviour is not just about physical aggression. It is also about quality of life and behaviours that limit someone's opportunities.
- Challenging behaviour always happens for a reason and we need to find out what that reason is.
- When we know why a behaviour occurs, we need to change the environment around the individual, teach them new skills and alternative ways of behaving, and react in an ethical way without punishing them.

References

Emerson E (1995) *Challenging Behaviour: Analysis and intervention in people with learning difficulties*. Cambridge: Cambridge University Press.

Chapter 2

Understanding and assessing behaviours that are described as challenging

Alick Bush

Behaviours that can cause harm or distress to someone with a learning disability or those around them are often very hard to make sense of and can result in people making responses that make the situation worse. It is important that we try to understand *why* we think someone is behaving as they are, before we try to intervene. This chapter gives support staff a framework for trying to understand why a behaviour occurs so that they can do things that will make it less likely to happen in the future. It describes what needs to be considered about the person, their environment, and the interactions between the person and those around them. It can often help to think about the behaviour as if it was communicating something to carers about what the person finds upsetting about their current situation.

Most behaviours can be understood if we have a good knowledge about the person, the environment they live in, and how the two can interact. Figure 2.1 highlights this interaction.

Figure 2.1: The interaction between a person, their environment and their behaviour

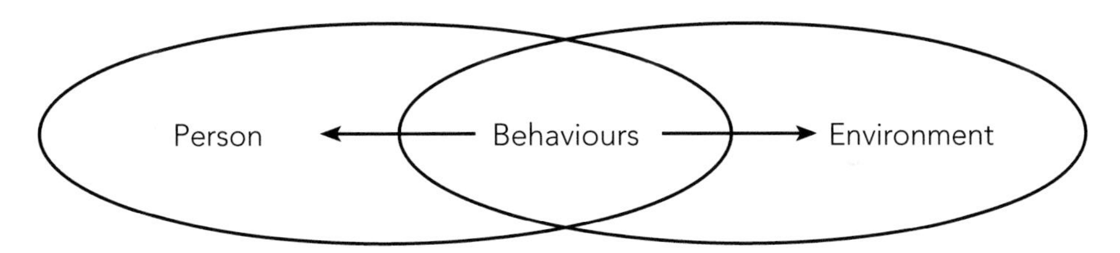

What do we need to know about the person?

It is important that staff get to know the person so that they understand their likes, dislikes and characteristics. Some of the factors that are important to know about the person include the following.

Personal characteristics

Many of us have routines and like things to be done in a specific way. Someone with autism may become distressed if something unexpected happens or if someone interacts with them in a particular way. If the person is unable to communicate that they don't like something, they may show their distress through behaviours that could be interpreted as being challenging.

Do we know what makes a good or a bad day for the person, and how do we support them to make sure that every day is a good day? If the person's level of disability makes it hard for them to exercise choice about what they do during the day, how do we know if they are enjoying what is available to them?

Health

Are there any specific health concerns that might be contributing to the person being upset or 'out of sorts'? If someone is in pain because of dental problems, constipation, period pains, indigestion, dehydration or headache, how is that going to affect their tolerance to things happening that they don't like?

Communication

How does the person make sense of what is happening around them? Do they understand what is expected when someone asks them to do something? They might understand a request when it is accompanied by the appropriate cues (pointing, beckoning etc), but what happens if it is an unusual request? What ways do they have to let you know when something is bothering them, and do support staff know how to interpret subtle changes in the person that might be their only way of communicating something to those around them?

Some of the other important characteristics about the person (eg. autism, mental health, epilepsy) will be explored in more detail in later chapters.

What do we need to know about their environment?

We need to try to understand the effect that the person's environment might be having on them. This can include the following factors.

Physical environment

How comfortable is it for the person to live where they are? How suitable are the heating, lighting and sound levels? Some people like noisy, busy, warm places, while others prefer the opposite. What do staff believe is the 'ideal environment' for the people they are supporting, and do they believe this is what the person experiences?

Activities and stimulation

How well does the current environment provide the level and type of stimulation that the person likes? Have the person's preferences and interests been fully taken into account when staff planned the activities that are available? Are opportunities available for the person to carry out activities with others? If a television is on where the person lives, do staff know if they find the programmes interesting, or does the constant background noise annoy them?

Interactions with people around them

Many people with learning disabilities have no choice over whom they live with or who supports them. People who show behaviour that is described as challenging are often grouped together with other people who have similar reputations. This can sometimes make for a noisy, frightening place where there are high levels of arousal and aggression, and few opportunities to develop positive relationships. How well do we think the person gets on with those around them? This question also applies to the person's relationship with those who are providing their support. Some people prefer energetic, vocal staff while others prefer calm and relaxed relationships. Do we know how well the support staff match the individual's preferences?

Behaviour as 'communication'

By gaining an understanding of the person, their environment and how these factors might interact and influence a person's behaviour, it starts to become possible to make sense of why a particular behaviour might be occurring.

A useful framework for bringing these factors together is to start to imagine that the person's challenging behaviour could be their way of communicating to the people around them about what their wishes or concerns might be. This is not to suggest that the person is able to work out what is wrong for them and is actively trying to communicate this message to others, but behaviour as communication can be a helpful analogy to explain why a behaviour might be occurring.

For anyone who is in distress, communicating that distress and the reasons for it is usually the starting point for resolving the situation. In the workplace it might be that someone tells their manager they are finding the work too difficult, and at home someone might tell their partner that they are getting tired of being taken for granted. However, a person with learning disabilities who has limited verbal communication is less likely to be able to put things right by communicating their situation to those who can make changes. For them, challenging behaviours might be the only – or the most effective – way of communicating that something is wrong.

There are likely to be many things that a person with learning disabilities might need to communicate to those around them, but as a starting point it is useful to explore a few of the messages that might reflect what unpleasant things the person could be experiencing. It can sometimes help to describe the behaviours as if they represented the person telling us what is wrong. At times of distress, few people can rationalise the cause of their distress. Someone with significant learning disabilities is even less likely to be able to do this. The task of support staff is to try to make a 'best guess' about what is happening and what we can interpret the behaviour as communicating to others. Some of the possible communications could include:

- *'I'm in pain and need help to remove the source of the pain'*
- *'I'm under-stimulated and need more sensory stimulation'*
- *'People are asking me to do things that I don't like or I don't understand what they want'*
- *'Things are happening around me that are frightening or that I don't like and I need it to stop'*
- *'I need more (or less) social interaction with people'*
- *'I need something tangible that I don't have (eg. a drink, food, activity).'*

The role of carers in understanding behaviour

The task of understanding what the challenging behaviour might be communicating is the responsibility of everyone who is a part of the person's life. The face-to-face support worker is important in this process as they have particular insights into the person's preferences and characteristics. Support staff are well placed to use their knowledge of the person to create hypotheses about what they think could be the reasons for the person showing behaviours that others find challenging.

It is helpful to have a systematic approach to gathering information about when and why a particular behaviour is occurring. Key questions are often helpful in forming a clear picture of what is going on, such as when does the behaviour not occur? Or gathering information about when the behaviour does occur.

When does the behaviour *not* occur?

This question is often overlooked as we can focus exclusively on the times when we are concerned about someone's behaviour. However, by having insights into the circumstances and situations when the behaviour is not happening, it can tell us what needs to be continued to avoid the behaviours in the future. It can also help us to identify when something has changed that might be a trigger for the behaviour. This provides valuable information about the possible reasons for the behaviour.

It can be helpful to consider what makes a good day for the person and whether there are particular times when the behaviour rarely occurs. This could include identifying the person's preferred activities, preferred support staff, preferred ways of being supported, and preferred ways of communicating. This information should be available within a person-centred support plan.

Gathering information about when the behaviour does occur

There are a number of ways that support staff can gather systematic information about the situations that lead to an increased likelihood of the challenging behaviour occurring. The starting point is usually good observations about what has led up to the behaviour, specific triggers for the behaviour, and what changed immediately after the behaviour as a consequence of it. This is not an easy task for direct carers who are likely to be focusing on managing the situation safely rather than trying to analyse what is happening. However, the more detailed the information that can be recorded at the time, the easier it is to identify patterns and reasons for the behaviour.

Sometimes it is useful to record information about the circumstances of the behaviour on an antecedent – behaviour – consequences (ABC) chart. ABC charts involve detailed recording of what happened immediately before and then after a particular behaviour. It is useful to consider this in relation to potential hypotheses about the reason for the behaviour. This might include the following questions.

- What was the person doing in the lead up to the behaviour? Could they have been bored with the activity, or had they been doing it for a long time etc?
- Had they been interrupted during a favourite activity and were they then prevented from continuing it?
- Was the environment uncomfortable, over-stimulating or under-stimulating?
- Did someone do something they don't like? This could include invading their space, taking something from them, or interfering with them.
- Were there too many demands being made of them, or was there insufficient stimulation and activity?
- Were any requests made to them that they might not have understood?
- Could they have been in discomfort or pain?

Case study: Yusef

Yusef has recently moved into a house with three other people who also have learning disabilities. Very little information has come with Yusef, and staff are unsure how best to support him in ways that will reduce the level of his challenging behaviour. He has very little verbal communication and needs assistance with many of his activities of daily living. He spends a lot of time rocking gently, but sometimes his rocking becomes more extreme and he will hit his head hard against the wall behind him, or on anything or anyone in front of him. There is no clear view about what the cause is of this behaviour, or guidance for staff about what to do when he starts to rock more vigorously, or what they can do to avoid it in the first place.

Yusef's new key worker is determined to find a better way to support him and she enlists the help of the community learning disability team (CLDT) to try to understand why he sometimes rocks so vigorously, risking injury to himself and others. They soon establish that there is an inconsistent approach to how to support him as no one really seems to know much about him.

Staff from the CLDT spend some time with Yusef and watch how people interact with him. They ask staff to complete an ABC chart to capture information about how often, and under what circumstances, the extreme rocking happens. A week later the CLDT staff and Yusef's key worker meet to review the information that they have gathered.

They believe that Yusef finds gentle rocking soothing and self-stimulating. Their observations are that the extreme rocking often happens when one of his particularly boisterous housemates jumps and shouts close to him. The team hypothesise that he may be afraid that he is going to be hurt when this occurs and that his extreme rocking has the effect of making people get away from him. Based on this hypothesis, staff work out ways that they can provide Yusef with a range of different forms of stimulation. They also work out how the boisterous resident can be encouraged to carry out his energetic activities in a different room. By reassuring Yusef that he is not going to be hurt by others in the house, his vigorous rocking gradually reduces.

Conclusion

- Before trying to change a person's behaviour, it is important to try to understand *why* it is happening.
- In order to do this we need a good knowledge of the person and their environment.
- A detailed person-centred plan is the starting point for understanding why a person might show behaviours that are described as challenging.
- It can be helpful to think about behaviour that challenges as if it is communicates something about a person's unmet needs or wishes.
- One useful way to understand why a behaviour occurs is to find out when it does *not* happen. It is important to gather systematic information about what factors contribute to the behaviour happening, and what the consequences of the behaviour are.

Further reading

Department of Health (2007) *Services for People with Learning Disabilities and Challenging Behaviour or Mental Health Needs* (Revised edition). London: TSO.

Royal College of Psychiatrists, British Psychological Society and Royal College of Speech and Language Therapists (2007) *Challenging Behaviour: A unified approach. Clinical and service guidelines for supporting people with learning disabilities who are at risk of receiving abusive or restrictive practices. College Report CR144.* London: RCPsych.

Chapter 3

Environmental interventions

Anne Parris and Karen Watson

This chapter looks at individuals whose behaviour is described as challenging within the context of their environment and how it may impact on their behaviour. In order to explain existing challenging behaviour, it is necessary to look at both the individual and the environments with which they interact (McGill & Toogood, 1994). This chapter will outline three different categories of environment and explore the idea of 'smoothing the fit' (LaVigna & Willis, 2005) between a person and their physical, interpersonal and programmatic (activity) environments. It will also describe how environmental interventions can bring about rapid, positive effects on challenging behaviours.

The environment

Environment can refer to physical factors, such as the layout of a room, the way a service is set up and organised and, on a more individual level, the physical environment and the quality of a person's life.

This chapter specifically focuses on environmental interventions in the context of the following three environmental categories.

1. **Physical:** the 'touchable', tangible or sensory aspects of a person's surroundings
2. **Interpersonal:** the social aspect of a person's surroundings, the people around them, their relationships, communication and interactions with others
3. **Programmatic:** the routines, skills and activities that are available to the person as well as those they actually engage in

If these three aspects of a person's environment are taken into consideration, it becomes clear how the environment in which we exist exerts a powerful influence on our well-being. The environment can determine a person's well-being and comfort and affect their behaviour, relationships, capacity to communicate, willingness to engage, and how well they do in activities.

The behaviour

When we think about people with learning disabilities whose behaviour is described as challenging, it is important to consider the possible reasons the person is engaging in these behaviours. This approach helps us to understand that 'behaviour' is often an attempt to gain some control over an environment or to communicate needs, often as a result of not having any other effective means of doing so.

When evaluating a person's environment, it is very important to bear in mind that, often, those individuals whose behaviour may be described as challenging have very little control over their lives. This may be as a result of having learning disabilities (often severe), communication difficulties and possibly additional physical disabilities or sensory impairments. A person whose behaviour is described as challenging will often not have a formal method of communicating their wishes and use the most effective and efficient ways at their disposal in order to makes changes in their environment.

Lack of control over one's environment may lead to a vicious cycle of behaviour. Environmental factors lead to an onset of behaviour that challenges others, which in turn lead to the person's environment becoming more restrictive (less access to activities, less control etc). This restrictive environment may in turn lead to an increase in behaviour, which may lead to further environmental restrictions etc. See Figure 3.1.

Figure 3.1: Cycle of restriction

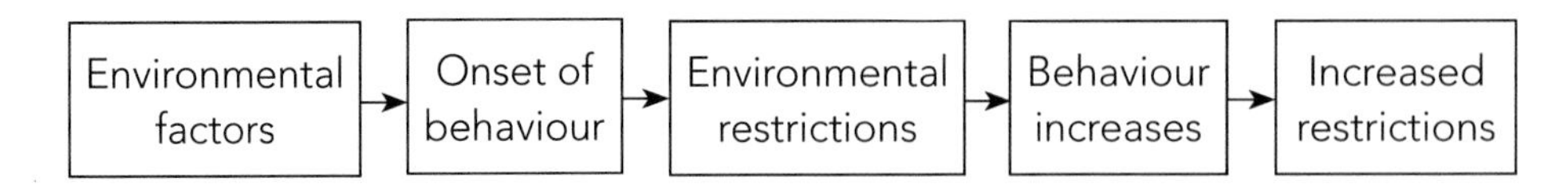

Behaviours that are considered challenging may become 'shaped up' over many years as the person learns that they have more impact. In other words, if a challenging behaviour always elicits a response from the environment, even if this is a negative response, the person whose behaviours are considered challenging may learn that people pay more attention to what they are 'saying' with their behaviour than to legitimate attempts at communication. For example, if a person is attempting to communicate that they want to be left alone, but these attempts are not being noticed by others, the person may then start to bang their head against a hard surface, which may result in others leaving them alone. Thus, this person's 'behaviour' has become far more effective in getting their message across to others.

It is easy to see that if someone is in a situation that they are finding difficult or uncomfortable, and they are not able to change this or express their dissatisfaction, then they may be much more likely to use 'behaviour' in order for things to change.

Functional analysis

In order to address any issues of concern, the first step is to identify how the environment and behaviour impact on each other. Functional analysis is an assessment process that identifies the function of a person's behaviour and how their environment maintains the behaviour.

The functions of behaviour fall in to following broad categories:

- to escape or avoid undesirable situations
- to increase social contact
- to adjust to levels of sensory stimulation
- to increase access to preferred objects or activities.

Table 3.1 gives examples of how an environment may have an impact on the possible functions of behaviour.

Table 3.1: Environmental impact on the possible functions of behaviour.

Behaviour maintained by:	Environment characterised by:
Escape or avoidance of undesirable situations	Intermittently high levels of social control and abuse
Increased social interaction	Low levels of social interaction
Sensory stimulation	Unstimulating environment (eg. lack of things to do)
Increased access to objects and activities	Control over access to objects and activities

(Adapted from McGill & Toogood, 1994)

A good assessment highlights the link between behaviours and these aspects of the environment. Once the links have been established and these factors have been considered, environmental interventions should be focused on making real changes to a person's life and improving their quality of life.

Environmental interventions and strategies

The following interventions are based on the Multi-element Model for Breaking the Barriers to Social and Community Integration (LaVigna & Willis, 2005). This model is based on both proactive and reactive strategies.

Proactive support strategies are focused on reducing the likelihood of challenging behaviour and allowing an individual to be as independent and successful as possible. This type of strategy includes environmental manipulations, positive programming (developing skills and activities, see Chapters 4 and 8) and focused support (interventions to directly reduce challenging behaviour, see Chapter 5). Reactive strategies provide guidelines to help those supporting a person to cope with the behaviour when it occurs (see Chapter 6). These are intended to be used in the short-term.

The interventions and strategies are examined in the context of the three main environment categories identified at the start of the chapter (physical, interpersonal and programmatic). It should be noted that these are not mutually exclusive and some factors may overlap. The following list of strategies and interventions is not exhaustive and there are many other ways in which a person's environment can be changed.

Within each of the three environmental categories, the possible strategies and interventions are presented as possible answers to a series of questions. For each question there is a rationale explaining why this is to be considered, followed by possible strategies and interventions.

Key	
?	The question
	Rationale
	Possible strategies and interventions

Physical environment

This refers to the 'touchable', tangible and sensory aspects of a person's surroundings. Factors to consider are covered in the following questions.

	**Is the physical space suitable for the person?**
	This may be a particularly important consideration for people with additional physical difficulties, which may include mobility or motor control as well as sensory difficulties. If a person cannot control their movements within the environment or the layout persistently prevents them doing things, they may become frustrated.
	■ Think about the physical environment in terms of the specific challenges it may present to a person. ■ For example, are there steps down to the kitchen that might prevent free access to a person with mobility difficulties? Think about a way this obstacle could be overcome. ■ Consider installing grab rails, which might enable someone with an unsteady gait to move around their home more independently, or removing rugs.

- Think about automatic door openers, width of doorways and space to manoeuvre for people who use wheelchairs. Think also about work surface heights. For example, is the person unable to make themselves a drink in the kitchen simply because there are no surfaces of a height suitable to wheelchair users?
- Consider whether the environment has equipment suitable for the person. Consider how adaptive equipment may provide a person with greater control. For example, a kettle tipper in the kitchen for someone with limited grip strength or an adapted remote control for someone's music system.
- Consider the furniture and whether or not it meets individual needs. For example, some people may not like sofas as they need the 'security' of an armchair or the physical sensation of a bean bag. Some people may like the vestibular stimulation of a rocking chair. People may also have fabric preferences, for example one person may not be able to tolerate nylon, whereas someone else may not like the uneven feel of corduroy.

Is the environment barren?

This could refer to the physical environment such as the décor, furnishings, pictures etc, which make our environment a pleasant place to be as well as giving us something to look at. It could also include whether there are activities and whether interaction with others is easily available for the person.

- Make the person's environment as pleasant as possible to be in. Wherever possible, involve the person in choosing decorations.
- Make sure there are pictures/photos on the walls. If there are concerns about people removing things, then murals painted directly onto walls may be an option.
- Consider the colour scheme and contrast. This may be particularly relevant to people with visual impairments who may benefit, for example, from strong contrasting paintwork on doorframes and skirting boards to help them 'make out' the edges of walls.
- Have activities easily accessible for the person. This could include things like puzzles, magazines, games, sensory objects as well as specific items that the person enjoys.
- Make sure that the person has frequent opportunities to be involved in activities.

- Make sure that the person has opportunities for interaction with others. This should include social interactions and not interactions solely based on functional needs, such as personal care.

Is the noise level appropriate for the person?

People have different tolerance levels to noise and some people find noise distressing. Some people may not be able to 'filter out' background noise such as people talking or music. Others may find particular sounds difficult to cope with (pitch and volume). These factors may prevent a person from concentrating or may be very stressful for them. This may be more of an issue if the person has sensory impairments/autism.

If a person is unable to control noise levels themselves, they may react by displaying behaviour that can be described as challenging.

- Think about the 'match' of residents living in the house. If there are people who prefer a quiet environment and others who prefer a noisier one, then are they suited to living together?
- Make sure the radio and television are not on at the same time.
- Make sure volume is at a level that is suitable for everyone. If this is not possible, make sure there is the option of a quiet space. For example, if there is not a separate room, within a sitting room it may be possible to create two separate areas by positioning furniture.
- Ensure there is no distracting background noise when you start an activity. For example, in a shared house, choose a time when other residents are out to support the person in an activity.
- Does the person need adaptive equipment or visual prompts to be able to turn the TV/stereo off (or turn down the volume)?
- If you are supporting someone out in the community, then try to go to places that aren't too noisy. If this is not possible, then strategies such as supporting the person to wear headphones to listen to music or being redirected into an activity may need to be considered.

Are the light levels appropriate for the person?

Some people are very sensitive to light and find bright lights (particularly strip lighting) difficult to cope with. However, some people may need bright lighting (especially if they have a visual impairment).

- Use lamps instead of main lights. This can make the lighting softer. Individual lamps can also more easily be adapted for differing requirements within the same room.
- When positioning lights/lamps be aware of possible glare or where shadow falls.
- Make sure that people can control the lighting themselves if they are able to, for example, are light switches accessible to someone in a wheelchair?
- If someone does need more light, then use main lights as well as spotlights to highlight specific areas of the house.
- Consider the colour of the walls, as some colours reflect light better than others.
- People may need different lighting at different times and for different reasons – make sure the light levels are appropriate for each individual at all times.

?

Is the temperature appropriate for the person?

Again, people have different tolerance levels to how hot or cold an environment is. Often people may feel warmer if they are active and moving about more. For example, a member of staff may feel hot because they are moving around the house, whereas a person with learning disabilities may be unable to or less likely move around, so will feel colder. Consideration also needs to given when the weather is hot/cold.

- Adjust the temperatures to suit the person. It may be appropriate to have areas of the environment at different temperatures.
- Do not move people into direct draughts (unless they like them) – be mindful of others when opening windows etc.
- If someone likes the heat, then make sure they are sitting in the warmest part of a room.

- Think about a person's clothing. For example, consider offering an additional sweater if it is cold.
- Use fans in the summer if it is too hot.
- Give the person hot/cold drinks (or better still, support them to make these themselves!).
- Make sure you are supporting the person to move around and be more active (if possible).

Is drink and food accessible?

Consideration needs to be given to why food and drink has been restricted in the first place and who this has been of benefit to. For example, is access to them restricted as a convenience to staff simply because access needs to be facilitated by a member of staff? Also, think about whether restrictions are in place that would not necessarily be there for someone without learning disabilities. Consider whether the restriction is on something that most people would take for granted as one of their liberties, such as being able to have a drink at any time as opposed to set times during the day. Behaviour targeted at accessing food may sometimes be present just because these things are restricted in the first place.

- Give the person more control over access to food/drink. This will include not locking the kitchen if there is no clinical need to do so, for example, if the person has Prader-Willi syndrome or if it has been done so for the convenience of staff.
- Try to ensure the person has a way of communicating that they would like food or drink and that staff understand this. This may be a word, a sound, a gesture or an object, for example, whatever is appropriate to the individual.
- Give the person regular access to food/drink.
- Consider ways of enabling people to know when they can get food/drink. Visual prompts or reminders may facilitate this.
- Make access to food and drink part of an activity for the person.
- If someone appears to be frequently focused on access to food/drink, then consider why this may the case. For example if it is because they have nothing else to do and think about, then it may help to explore ways of increasing the interaction and activities available.

- Consider whether someone's medication may make them thirsty/hungry and think about how best to support this. Discussions with medical staff may help this process.

Interpersonal environment

This refers to the person's social surroundings and their relationships and interactions with others. Factors to consider are covered in the following questions.

Does everyone know how to communicate with the person?

Very often, those supporting people with learning disabilities overestimate how much they understand. This is because people are able to 'pick up' on lots of clues around the environment to help them assign meaning to speech. For example, when someone is asked to go and get ready for a bath, if the person supporting them has already turned on the water, which the person can hear, the person always has a bath at the same time of the day and they can smell their bubble bath, then the person does not necessarily need to understand the words that the person supporting them has used to prompt them into the activity.

Consideration also needs to be given to how attempts the person makes to communicate are 'listened to' by others. If these are missed, then the person may engage in behaviour that can be a challenge to manage as a result.

- Does the person have an up-to-date communication assessment? If not, then consider referring them to a speech and language therapy service for a communication assessment. This will highlight what the person can understand, how they express themselves and recommend strategies to support a person's communication environment.
- Ensure that staff communicate in a consistent manner.
- Ensure that attempts at communication by the person are not ignored or overlooked.
- Ensure all staff have attended the relevant training.

Does everyone know how to support the person?

Very often people with learning disabilities have lots of different people who support them. This can include family, friends, staff at college or workplaces, and different types of paid support workers, which may include residential staff, day centre staff, outreach support and bank/agency support workers etc. There may also be a high turnover of people who are paid to support the person. This may result in inconsistent knowledge about the person, which then may lead to inconsistent support. Inconsistent support may often lead to an increase in confusion and anxiety for the person, which may then, in turn, impact on any behaviour that may challenge others. Also, can the people supporting the person distinguish between care and support? This will give you an important insight to how they may then interact with the person.

- Having up-to-date information about the person is crucial. Whenever this is being reviewed, ensure that all people involved with the person have an opportunity to contribute. Different people may have different perspectives.
- Pull together all the relevant information into an 'all about me book'. This should include how the person likes to be supported, things that they can do for themselves and things that they need support with (highlighting what kind of support this may be), likes and dislikes, information about their health and any medication, how to communicate with the person and how to respond to any incidents of behaviour which is described as challenging.
- This information should be kept where staff have easy access to it, rather than in a file that no one looks at in the office.
- Everyone should make sure that any new bank or agency staff are familiar with this information.
- A smaller copy with the salient points could be kept with the person themselves. Consider who is going to see it and how much information they need. For example, there may be intimate information in the main book, which only staff supporting the person at home need to know and not tutors at college.
- Ensure all staff have attended relevant training.
- Ensure staff have adequate supervision.

What type of interactions does the person have?

Very often, people have very functional, task-orientated interactions with others. Consideration needs to be given as to how much opportunity we give to people with learning disabilities to have sociable interactions, without necessarily having an end result.

- Make sure that the person has regular opportunities to spend time with someone without an end result. Be careful that this is done in a way that the person is able to understand (by using intensive interaction, looking through their personal profile, as above, looking at magazines together, chatting about how their day was etc).

What are the expectations for the person?

This may link in with whether the person is being supported or cared for. There is a difference between whether someone is expected to be fully engaged in activities so that they can have a sense of achievement to those where they are considered too disabled to be able to do any of this. Getting the balance of expectation is crucial for success for that person. Too high and the person may not be able to reach the goal set, too low and the expectation may not be there in the first place. Also, consider who has set the agenda for these expectations.

- Identify the person's strengths and interests. Then try to link this is with supporting them in an activity.
- Think about the person's difficulties and what kind of support they may need to achieve success, for example, is any adaptive equipment needed, types of support such as verbal, gestural or hand-over-hand support.
- Give the person a variety of opportunities to participate in an activity. It may need to be repeated several times for the person to become familiar with it. However, if the person is not enjoying it after several attempts, then is it a worthwhile thing to do for the person, or does the support need to change in some way?
- Does everyone supporting the person have the same expectations?

Is the person lonely?

People with learning disabilities are more likely to be socially isolated. This is especially true for people whose behaviour is described as challenging.

A lot of people with learning disabilities have very small social networks: family members and those paid to support them may make up the majority of relationships that the person has. Also, a lot of people may have been placed in services that are a long way from their family, which may impact on possible feelings of loneliness.

- Support the person to have regular contact with their family. This may mean supporting them to visit or meet for coffee/lunch at a mutually convenient place, or it could mean regular opportunities for telephone contact.
- Identify any social events that the person could go to meet other people. Some people may like to meet up with other people with learning disabilities, others may not.
- Think about what the person likes doing and how this could be used to help the person meet others, for example, if someone likes football, then they could join a supporters club or become a regular at the local pub to watch the football games on TV.
- Regular access to local amenities will help develop relationships within the people's community.

Does the person only get what they want when they engage in behaviour that is described as challenging?

It is really important to recognise that if people are given the opportunity to engage in preferred activities only when they display challenging behaviours, then they are much more likely to use this method as a way of getting what they want. However, if these opportunities are present regardless of whether the person is engaging in a behaviour that is challenging for others, then the behaviour may become redundant, as it is no longer serves the function of getting what they want.

It is really important that access to preferred activities/interactions are not based on how a person behaves, for example, if they behave 'appropriately', then they get to go out for dinner. Nobody has the right to determine that we have to 'be good' in order to do what we want to do.

- The person should have regular access to preferred activities and interactions with others.
- Do not withdraw any planned activities/interactions with the person as a result of any behaviour that has been described as challenging. It may be necessary to wait until the person has calmed down, but the activity/interaction should always take place.

How do others 'behave' towards the person?

This can include staff, other people with learning disabilities and family members. Think about how people describe the person, particularly if they have become reduced to descriptions of their behaviours. Consider how it would feel to be described to others purely based on behaviour. It is important to remember that behaviour always occurs for a reason (although sometimes this may be hard to work out). How do others behave in response to the person's behaviour that is described as challenging?

- Be respectful.
- Always identify the positive qualities of the person, things that they like doing and what they are good at.
- Do not focus on the person's behaviour that may be described as challenging. Spend time with the person, doing what they like to do and engaging them in activities. This may help build up a more positive relationship between the person and the support worker.

Have there been any changes in the person's life recently?

Any change for a person with learning disabilities may have a significant impact on them. This can include changes such as a change of environment, changes within the team supporting them, changes in the person's routine, changes in the person's health. It can also include smaller changes such as a change in the way they are supported (inconsistent support).

- If changes are going to be made, then the service needs to have a plan in place about how to support the person through these changes.
- Tell the person about the changes (in a way they can understand).

Programmatic environment

The programmatic environment refers to the routines, skills and activities of a person. Factors to consider are covered in the following questions.

What activities is the person supported to be engaged in?

It is important to look at how often people are supported to be engaged in activities as boredom can have a major influence on whether someone may engage in behaviour which is described as challenging.

Also, it may be that the person is engaged in lots of activities, but these may be the same activities over and over again, which may become very boring. For example, someone may have a high level of household activities but little variety of any other types of activities.

Regardless of disability and behaviour, people are always able to engage in parts of an activity, if they are not able to engage in an activity from beginning to end.

- Encourage people to participate in any activity that takes place within the environment.
- Break the activity down into steps and support the person to participate in particular steps.
- Work together with the person to make the activity successful and a positive experience for them.
- Offer the person a variety of activities – do not concentrate on one type of activity.
- Think of new activities for the person – be creative.
- Use positive risk-management tools to enable the person to do more/different activities.

How are the activities presented to the person?

Does the person understand what they are being asked to do? Very often, people may not understand what is happening and what is expected of them, which may increase anxiety levels and therefore may increase the likelihood of behaviour that may be challenging to others occurring.

- Use a visual timetable for the person. Ideally this should be one where the photos are removable, to allow the person some flexibility about what they are doing.
- Keep the timetable in a place that is accessible to the person.
- Make the 'situation speak for itself' – before supporting the person into an activity, get everything ready beforehand (equipment needed, ingredients etc), for example if the person will be making a sandwich, then set out the bread, knife, plate and filling, ready for the person to get involved.
- Show the person a visual representation of the activity (object of reference, photo, picture etc) before prompting them into the activity.
- Make sure the activity takes place in the most appropriate and natural setting, for example making a cup of tea in the person's own kitchen rather than in a classroom at the local college.
- Allow the person to have regular breaks if necessary.

How does the person know when the activity will start and finish?

Very often, activities do not necessarily have clear beginnings and endings, for example supporting someone to do 'the housework', which could go on endlessly, as opposed to making the bed that may be much clearer for the person. Again, this may lead to the person becoming anxious about when the activity will end and indeed what will happen when it does.

- Chunk activities into singular ones, rather than activities that can merge into one, long activity.
- To start the activities, show the person a visual representation of the activity.
- Design a visual sequence of the activity. This will help the person identify the steps of the activity and get a sense of the order of the activity.

- Make sure the activity has a clear end. This could include the activity ending with something tangible, for example a cup of tea/sandwich (if that is the activity). It may be possible to teach the person the Makaton sign for 'finish' or have this in another visual format. If the person is using a visual timetable, then support the person to remove the photo of the activity they have just completed.
- Ensure staff have attended the relevant activities engagement or skills development training.

What type of support is needed?

People will need different types of support. The general types of support include physical support such as hand-over-hand guidance, gestural prompts such as pointing or modelling, verbal prompts where the instructions are said to the person. The types of prompts may vary for each activity. They may also change as the person becomes more familiar with the activity, for example the person may need physical prompts to begin with, but after doing the activity a few times, they may just need a verbal reminder.

- Try the activity out with the person to see what types of prompt they may need at certain stages of the activity.
- Make sure that everyone supporting the person knows the type of prompt needed, otherwise there will be a danger that too much or too little support is given to the person.
- Ensure that all staff have attended the relevant training.

What are the expectations for the person and the activity?

It is really important that the activity offered to the person is achievable for them.

- Break the activity down into steps. Record clearly which steps the person can do themselves, which they need support with (and whether this is physical, verbal, gestural etc) and which steps the person supporting them needs to do. Doing it this way will help to ensure that the activity provides the person with a sense of achievement.

Is the routine flexible?

Routine in life is important. This is more so for people with learning disabilities (particularly those who also have autism) as it makes things much more predictable for them. However, there does need to be some flexibility within this structure to allow the person to have control and choice over what they do, for example, is it essential that they make their bed every morning, or can it wait until later in the day if the person does not want to do it in the morning?

- Allow the person more choice about what they do and when they do it (be careful that 'choice' does not come to mean that the person is not involved in any activity!).
- Allow more time for activities to take place, particularly if the person likes to have regular breaks during the activity.
- Use timetables with the person, so they can decide for themselves what activities they would like to do and when these will happen.
- Consider a person's 'natural clock'. If the person does not like mornings then avoid planning more demanding activities straight after breakfast.

This chapter has been designed to offer some practical strategies to help support people with learning disabilities whose behaviour is described as challenging. It is not an exhaustive list; many more strategies could be added. Once people are able to think about some of the possible reasons that a person may engage in behaviour that poses a challenge for others, then the intervention may be something very simple.

Conclusion

- The environment can determine a person's well-being and comfort and as such, affect their behaviour, their relationships, their capacity to communicate, their willingness to engage and how well they do in activities.
- Assessment can identify the link between a person whose behaviour is described as challenging and the environment in which they live.
- Interventions focus on making changes to the person's physical, interpersonal and programmatic environment.

- Effective communication with the person and others is really important.
- Think about how you can support the person to have more control over their environment.
- Consistency of support is essential.

References

LaVigna G & Willis T (2005) Multi element model for breaking the barriers to social and community integration. *Tizard Learning Disability Review* **10** (2) 16–23.

McGill P & Toogood S (1994) Organising community placements. In: E Emerson, P McGill and J Mansell (Eds) *Severe Learning Disabilities and Challenging Behaviours: Designing high quality services*. Gateshead: Stanley Thornes.

Chapter 4

Communication and challenging behaviour

Jill Bradshaw

Communication is a key area in understanding not only why challenging behaviour occurs but also how we can try to prevent challenging behaviour happening in the future (Bradshaw, 2002). Most people with learning disabilities have difficulty communicating. This includes being able to understand what other people are communicating and being able to express themselves. We also know from research that challenging behaviours often increase (either in frequency, intensity or duration) when communication difficulties increase (Bott *et al,* 1997).

Why is communication so important?

The following case study will help you to consider ways in which communication difficulties may have led to challenging behaviour.

Case study: Winston

Winston is a 40-year-old British black man with severe learning disabilities. He lives at home with his parents and attends a local day centre five days a week. Winston enjoys being outside and playing sports. He particularly likes football. He also enjoys spending time with members of staff.

Winston's challenging behaviours include hitting, kicking and biting people. These behaviours typically occur four or five times a week, almost always at the day centre, during times when Winston is left with little to do. The psychology team have assessed Winston and think that Winston's behaviours serve the function of access to staff attention and access to preferred activities. After an incident of challenging behaviour, Winston is often taken outside, by a member of staff who has a particularly good relationship with him, to play football. Staff at the day centre think that this is a good way for Winston to get rid of some of his energy.

Winston communicates using short phrases of one or two words. He also knows some signs but doesn't often use these unless he is prompted by other people. He is able to understand simple sentences. He has good understanding of words that relate to people, places or events (for example, names of people, shops, swimming etc). He understands when people talk to him about what is happening, or what is about to happen. He has much more difficulty in understanding when the staff talk about things that are (or in this example, are not) going to happen in the future. Winston also has difficulty understanding words which relate to emotions, negatives (for example, not) and time concepts (for example, tomorrow). For example, if staff say 'Winston, we are not swimming tomorrow, so you don't need to bring your trunks' then Winston will probably only understand 'swimming' and think that he is going swimming. In his experience, the most likely outcome of someone talking to him about swimming is that they are about to take him swimming. He is able to understand photographs and these are sometimes used with him.

Yesterday there was an incident of challenging behaviour. Winston had had a busy morning gardening and had come into the centre to eat something. He had finished his meal quite quickly and was waiting for the afternoon activity. Winston repeatedly approached different members of staff saying 'football'. This happened five or six times. The staff were all busy and so typically responded by saying 'not yet mate' or 'not at the moment Winston' or 'we'll play football later' or 'you've just been outside, you can't play yet'. Winston became more agitated and eventually kicked and hit a member of staff. They were not seriously hurt. A member of staff was able to calm Winston down by taking him outside to play football.

Before you read on, stop and think about the following question.

- What communication factors do you think might have contributed to Winston's challenging behaviour?
  - Winston was using the communication skills he has to ask to play football (by saying 'football') but his requests were not successful.
  - Winston probably didn't understand the staff when they told him that he couldn't play football yet. The staff used words like 'later', 'not', and 'can't', which Winston is not able to understand.

In this situation, Winston had used his communication skills to ask for what he wanted. As staff were not able to meet his request, Winston eventually became more and more frustrated and then displayed challenging behaviour. This behaviour not only resulted in him getting his preferred activity, it also resulted in him spending time with staff. This makes it more likely that Winston will display challenging behaviour the next time this situation occurs as his challenging behaviour was successful in getting his needs met. This means he is learning that challenging behaviour is more effective than communication in getting his needs met.

Common communication difficulties that may contribute to challenging behaviour

Challenging behaviour may occur for a variety of reasons. Communication difficulties often contribute to an incident of challenging behaviour. Even when people have relatively good communication skills, strong emotions (such as fear, anger or frustration) are likely to have an impact on communication. In these situations, people will often have more difficulties listening, understanding and expressing themselves.

Difficulties understanding communication

People may not understand what they are being asked to do, or when they are being asked to do it. People may not know what is happening. This may be a particular issue in novel and unfamiliar situations. People may misunderstand and expect something different to happen (Kevan, 2003). People are often unable to let you know that they haven't understood.

Difficulties with expressive communication

Challenging behaviour is more likely to occur when people find it difficult to communicate (Macleod *et al,* 2002). People may not have the communication skills necessary to communicate their needs, express their feelings, make choices, and explain that they haven't understood what is expected of them (Bradshaw, 2005).

Some people may have very inconsistent ways of communicating and it may be difficult to interpret what they might mean (Grove *et al,* 1999).

What can be done to improve communication?

Improving communication can be effective in reducing challenging behaviours (Bopp *et al,* 2004). Before you read on, stop and think about the case study again.

- What communication strategies could the staff have used to help in this situation?
  - Staff could have used a visual timetable to explain to Winston when football was happening. This is something that would need to be developed over time.
  - Instead of telling Winston that he was not doing, they could have told him what was happening at the moment, for example, 'We're having lunch now'. Again, this could have been reinforced with the addition of photographs or signs.
  - Everyone has different needs for attention at different times. As Winston clearly wanted to be with a member of staff at that time, it would have been better if a member of staff had spent time with Winston immediately, in response to his verbal request. While this is not always easy to achieve, the reality is that if staff don't spend the time with the person then, they will have to spend the time with the person later anyway, dealing with the challenging behaviour.

Common communication interventions that may help to reduce challenging behaviour

Many of the interventions around communication are no different from what makes a good communication environment in services in general. However, creating a good communication environment is even more important in services for people whose behaviour is described as challenging. Skilled communication partners are those who enable the person with learning disabilities to make the most of the communication skills they have (Bartlett & Bunning, 1997). Try to think about where, when and with whom the person communicates best. Is there anything you can learn from this?

General communication strategies include:

- try to get the person's attention (for example, use their name before you start to speak, or if appropriate, use a touch cue)
- use simple language
- try to give one piece of information at a time to allow the person time to process what you are saying (for example, say 'Craig, sit down' and wait for this to happen before giving the next instruction, instead of 'come and sit down now Craig, because your food will be here in a minute')
- focus on what you want the person to do rather than on what you don't want them to do (for example, say 'walk' rather than 'don't run')
- where possible, back-up spoken communication with additional visual means (for example, signs, symbols, photographs and objects); your local speech and language therapist will be able to advise you on what visual means are likely to be most helpful and on how these can be introduced
- focus communication on what is happening or what is just about to happen (talking about future events may be confusing for the person)
- try to have a consistent approach to communication; where people have few or inconsistent methods of communication it can be very difficult if everyone interprets these signals in different ways; it is helpful if communication partners share information and try to agree on an approach; communication passports can be very helpful (Millar & Aitken, 2003) as these contain relevant information about the ways in which the person communicates
- try to respond positively to any attempts to communicate
- think about communicative alternatives to challenging behavior; this is known as functional communication training (Carr & Durand, 1985); communicative alternatives are ways that the person can request 'something', instead of engaging in challenging behaviour, for example see Table 4.1
- make sure that communication is more effective than challenging behaviour.

Table 4.1: Functions of behaviour and alternative communication

Possible function of behaviour	Example of possible alternative communication
To avoid difficult demands	Teach person to say 'help' or to hold up a card that says 'I need a break'
To gain attention	Teach person to put their hand up
To access a desired activity or object	Teach person a sign for desired activity or object

Of course, there are many other factors and strategies that you could use that do not just focus on communication. The most effective strategies will be those that include a multidisciplinary approach, and are worked out in collaboration with the support staff.

The majority of people who have learning disabilities and behaviour described as challenging will also have some communication difficulties. The ability to communicate including using speech, and the ability to understand what people are saying will reduce in times of stress (Bradshaw, 2002). This is particularly likely to be the case during incidents of challenging behaviour when people may well not be able to understand information that they are usually able to understand with ease.

It is important to think about how you are communicating and to make sure that people with learning disabilities are able to understand you. You can help by using simple language, presenting one piece of information at a time, using short sentences and supporting what you are saying with photographs, signed communication, symbols and objects where possible. Creating a good communication environment is important (Bradshaw, 1998). Good communication is even more important in situations where challenging behaviour may occur.

It is also important to think about all the different ways that the person with learning disabilities is able to communicate. When challenging behaviours occur, people with learning disabilities may need additional support to express their thoughts and feelings. You may need to be even more aware of changes in body language and facial expression. The person may need to rely on you to interpret their communication. It is important that you make communicating as easy as possible during such times. In order to reduce challenging behaviour, you need to make sure that you respond to and reinforce any attempts to communicate (Mirenda, 1997).

Conclusion

- Find out as much as you can about the person's communication skills.
- Try to make sure that everyone has a consistent approach to communicating with the person.
- Make communication as easy as possible, particularly during times when challenging behaviour is likely.
- Think about the function (for example, gaining attention, avoiding difficult demands) that the challenging behaviour may have for the person. Does the person have any other ways of communication this?

References

Bartlett C & Bunning K (1997) The importance of communication partnerships: A study to investigate the communicative exchanges between staff and adults with learning disabilities. *British Journal of Learning Disabilities* **25** 148–153.

Bopp KD, Brown KE & Mirenda P (2004) Speech-language pathologists' roles in the delivery of positive behavior support for individuals with developmental disabilities. *American Journal of Speech-Language Pathology* **13** 5–19.

Bott C, Farmer R & Rhode J (1997) Behaviour problems associated with lack of speech in people with learning disabilities. *Journal of Learning Disability Research* **41** 3–7.

Bradshaw J (1998) Assessing and intervening in the communication environment. *British Journal of Learning Disabilities* **26** 62–66.

Bradshaw J (2002) The management of challenging behaviour within a communication framework. In: A Budarham & A Hurd (Eds) *Management of Communication Needs of People with Learning Disability.* London: Whurr Publishers.

Bradshaw J (2005) The role of communication in person-centred planning. In: P Cambridge & S Carnaby (Eds) *Person Centred Planning and Care Management with People with Learning Disabilities.* London: Jessica Kingsley Publishers.

Carr, EG & Durand VM (1985) Reducing behavior problems through functional communication training. *Journal of Applied Behavior Analysis* **18** 111–126.

Kevan F (2003) Challenging behaviour and communication difficulties. *British Journal of Learning Disabilities* **31** 75–80.

Grove N, Bunning K, Porter J & Olsson C (1999) See what I mean: interpreting the meaning of communication by people with severe and profound learning disabilities. *Journal of Applied Research in Learning Disabilities* **12** 190–203.

Macleod FJ, Morrison F, Swanston M & Lindsay W (2002) Effects of relocation on the communication and challenging behaviours of four people with severe learning disabilities. *British Journal of Learning Disabilities* **30** 32–37.

Millar S & Aitken S (2003) *Personal Communication Passports.* Edinburgh: University of Edinburgh CALL Centre.

Mirenda P (1997) Supporting individuals with challenging behaviour through functional communication training and AAC: research review. *Augmentative and Alternative Communication* **13** 207–225.

Chapter 5

Focused support strategies

Peter Baker and John Shephard

The therapeutic approach for people with learning disabilities who present challenging behaviour that has the strongest evidence base is arguably applied behaviour analysis (ABA). Many exponents of ABA rejected the use of punishment-based strategies and argued for comprehensive, multi-element-based interventions. LaVigna and Willis's (1995) multi-element model was one of the pioneering influences in what is now known as positive behaviour support (PBS). They described a process whereby the individual has a broad and comprehensive person-centred assessment, which aims to understand the meaning of their behaviour. On the basis of this assessment a support plan is constructed, which includes proactive strategies designed to change the behaviour over time, and reactive strategies to deal with situations when they occur. PBS underpins the recent clinical and service guidance issued by the British Psychological Society, the Royal College of Psychiatry and the Royal College of Speech and Language Therapists (RCP, 2007).

This chapter examines focused support, also known as 'direct treatment strategies' (the two terms are used interchangeably by LaVigna & Willis, 1995). The primary goal is to establish rapid control over the behaviour in order to reduce the associated risks. These risks are often those involved with reacting to the behaviour. The three main categories of focused support strategies are the use of differential reinforcement schedules, removal and/or altering antecedent conditions, and non-contingent reinforcement.

Differential reinforcement schedules

These techniques are designed to reduce the frequency of the behaviour by deliberate (and arguably artificial) manipulation of the environmental events that control the behaviour.

Differential reinforcement of other behaviour (DRO)

In this technique a reinforcer is offered to the individual if, after a specified period, the target behaviour was not performed. The technique is called the 'differential reinforcement of other behaviour' as any such schedule would involve the differential reinforcement of any behaviour the individual produced during this interval *other* than the targeted behaviour. In order to implement such a schedule, the target behaviour would need to be precisely defined, with the time interval identified and a reinforcer selected.

There are three main types of reinforcement schedule:

- DRO fixed interval
- DRO reset
- DRO progressive.

DRO fixed interval schedule

In the DRO fixed interval schedule an individual is provided with a reinforcer for every pre-determined time period in which they do not produce the target behaviour. At the end of the interval a reinforcer is delivered if the individual has not produced the target behaviour, and not delivered if the behaviour has occurred. This procedure is repeated at the end of each time interval. This procedure may be useful in order to establish initial control over the behaviour.

DRO reset schedule

In a DRO reset schedule the individual is again provided with a reinforcer for every pre-determined time period in which there is no target behaviour. In this case, if the target behaviour occurs the clock is reset and the interval starts again. This procedure is thought to be more useful for higher frequency behaviours. A potential side effect may well be that the delivery of the reinforcer may become a trigger for the target behaviour. The individual could deduce that they can engage in the target behaviour immediately after they have received the reinforcer, with only the minimum of inconvenience, as the clock would only have been running for a short period and its reset would not have an impact.

DRO progressive schedule

In the DRO progressive schedule the individual earns increasing units of reinforcers (up to a pre-determined level) for each consecutive period of no behaviours. This schedule is particularly useful for low frequency behaviours and avoids the phenomena whereby the delivery of the reinforcer becomes the trigger for challenging behaviour.

In general, fixed interval schedules should be used to establish initial control. For higher frequency behaviours, reset schedules should be used and with lower frequency behaviours, the DRO progressive schedule should be used. Once the interventions are working and the behaviour is under control, the intervals can be gradually increased. Once the intervention is terminated, non-contingent access to the reinforcer should be routinely scheduled.

The initial selection of the time interval in a DRO is crucial. If it is too long, the individual will not experience enough of the reinforcer to motivate them; and if it is too short they will experience too much, thus affecting motivation, with the inherent danger that they might consider displaying target behaviours with little cost to themselves. LaVigna and Donnellan (1986) proposed the Goldilocks rule in order to make decisions about the length of the interval in order to get it 'just right'. They advised that the interval should be half the average length of time between behaviours, the inter-response time (IRT). In the example presented, the behaviour occurs 10 times in a five-hour period – thus the IRT is 30 minutes. The optimum interval would be half of this time ie. 15 minutes. With this interval the individual would come into contact with the reinforcer for 50% of the time, even if they continued to behave at the same frequency, thus giving them enough experience of the reinforcer to motivate them.

Differential reinforcement of low rates of behaviour (DRL)

These procedures are typically used in situations where the target behaviour is defined as problematic by reference to its frequency.

There are two types of usage:

- IRT (inter-response time) method
- low rates method.

IRT schedules

DRL IRT schedules are used in situations where the behaviour is considered to be OK, but occurs too often. For example, a child in a classroom interrupting the teacher to ask questions is OK, but if this was to happen every two minutes it would be extremely disruptive and problematic.

A pre-determined interval is selected and the goal would be for the individual not to engage in the target behaviour during this period of time.

Dependant on the individual and the circumstances, it may well be that an explanation is provided to the individual that a sufficient period of time has not elapsed and that no reinforcement will be forthcoming. As the performance improves, the interval would be gradually increased, with the expectation that the individual is able to tolerate increasing periods without presenting the target behaviour.

Low rates method

DRL low rates method is used in circumstances where, for whatever reason, the goal would be to reduce the frequency of the behaviour. This may be because the behaviour is defined as problematic by reference to it occurring too often. Alternatively, the behaviour is generally considered problematic, but is so frequent that other types of reinforcement schedules would be impractical to implement.

A pre-determined interval would be selected and the individual would receive reinforcement if they emitted fewer than a pre-determined number of behaviours. The level is initially set by ascertaining the mean number of behaviours that would usually occur, thus the individual would have a 50% chance of experiencing the reinforcer when the programme started.

Donnellan *et al* (1988) recommend that concrete, tangible feedback systems are used. For example, a glass jar with table tennis balls might be used. The number of balls in the jar at the beginning of the interval would be set as the number of pre-determined behaviours. Every time the behaviour occurs, a ball is removed (preferably by the individual themselves) and the individual is reassured that they still have more opportunities to earn the reinforcer – providing no behaviour occurs within the designated time period. As long as at least one ball remains at the end of the period, the individual will receive the reinforcer.

The advantage of using DRL schedules is that intervals can be arbitrarily determined so that they fit in with naturally occurring periods in the day, such as lesson periods in a school day. In addition, DRL low rates can be used with more than one individual. For example, this could be used to manage the behaviour of a group of students in a classroom.

Differential reinforcement of alternative responses (DRA)

These are also referred to as differential reinforcement of incompatible responses (DRI) or alternative response (ALT-R) schedules. These involve the systematic reinforcement of specified alternative behaviours. This is a simple idea, but in order to maximise the chances of being effective these should ideally be behaviours that are physically incompatible with the target behaviour ie. it would be impossible for the individual to perform the target behaviour and the alternative response at the same time. For example, with the target behaviour of hand to head self-injury, having both hands in pockets would be incompatible. Thus there might be specific circumstances where this type of intervention might be indicated – perhaps this might be used at certain times that the behaviour has been identified as being highly likely to occur or times that it was considered to be especially risky.

Implementation issues

The selection of the reinforcer is key as it must be powerful enough to outweigh the motivation the person has for engaging in the challenging behaviour. Ideally, it should be the same reinforcer the person uses their challenging behaviour to obtain. In addition, it should only be available through the schedule and therefore not available at all other times. Furthermore, in order to maximise its motivational power, even with perfect performance of 100% no behaviours, the maximum amount of reinforcer should still be less than the person would want if they had free access. For example, if the reinforcer was chocolate and if given free access the individual would eat three bars a day, the maximum reinforcement should be no greater than two bars. A further challenge to ensure ethical implementation of these procedures is that the reinforcers should be additional and something that is added to the life of the person and not something they have had or should have by right.

While the use of differential reinforcement strategies holds a great deal of promise, there are certain procedural considerations that may well be difficult to overcome. This may, on occasion, render them unfit for the ascribed purpose – that is to produce the most rapid effects possible. High levels of supervision of the individual are required in order that all occurrences and non-occurrences of the behaviour are noted and responded to accordingly. Many services do not have the organisation or competencies to deliver such schedules, thus clinicians are often required to spend considerable resources and time setting up such programmes. This represents a major challenge in delivering the necessary rapid effects.

It is also often difficult to find effective reinforcers. The major challenge would appear to be finding reinforcers that would be powerful enough to compete with the highly 'driven' nature of some challenging behaviours. Furthermore, once these have been identified they need to be deliverable, and something the person does not access ordinarily (ie. restricted to use within the schedule). This may raise serious ethical concerns as the schedule effectively rations something that is highly desirable for the individual.

The non-constructional nature of many of the schedules is a further concern. As indicated earlier, considerable resources may be required to set up such interventions and, as such, this may not be considered justified if the individual does not acquire new skills. It is also not necessary to understand why the individual is engaging in the behaviour in order to implement many of these strategies. While this could be advantageous in situations where the reasons for the behaviour are unclear, there is an obvious danger that people will not be motivated to seek to understand. This is a serious concern as research would indicate that having an understanding of the reasons for the behaviour is one of the most important factors that would predict a good outcome for the individual with learning disabilities and challenging behaviour (Didden *et al,* 1997)

Antecedent interventions

These types of interventions necessitate that an assessment of the behaviour is carried out so that the antecedent conditions that trigger or set the occasion for the behaviour are identified. Where possible this can be removed, thus achieving rapid control over the behaviour. For example, if the behaviour is triggered by a specific request to engage in an activity, simply not making this request would reduce the occurrence of the behaviour, thus potentially achieving the ascribed role of rapid control of behaviour. This need not necessarily be a permanent removal of the demand, indeed the demand may be systematically reintroduced, albeit in a modified and perhaps less aversive form. For a more in-depth discussion of procedures aimed at modifying demands, see Miltenberger (2006).

In situations where removal is not possible, alteration of the antecedent condition may well have the same effect. Horner *et al* (1997) used the term 'neutralising routines' to describe this type of alteration of antecedent conditions. They demonstrated that, for some of the participants in their study, being told that a planned activity was cancelled or delayed and then being requested to comply in another task was an antecedent condition for distressed and problematic behaviour. Similarly, for another participant, getting less than five hours' sleep has a similar effect on their behaviour when combined with a request to comply.

The first participants were given the opportunity to engage in a preferred alternative activity and to formally reschedule the cancelled activity prior to the requests for compliance. The last individual was given a one-hour nap prior to the request. Both procedures effectively reduced the problem behaviours. In such a situation we can assume that events such as the cancellation of an activity and not getting enough sleep were absolutely unavoidable. When these events occurred they affected the individual's motivation to engage in the presented tasks to such an extent that they exhibited difficult and problematic behaviours. If the option of not presenting the demand was available, this would have been an example of removal of an aspect of the antecedent condition. However, this was not possible, hence the need for alteration of a further aspect of the antecedent condition, and the use of effective neutralising routines to minimise the problematic behaviours.

Alternatively, presenting the reinforcer independently of the behaviour can be implemented in order to alter the link between them. This will usually be achieved by delivering large amounts of the reinforcer at times determined by the clock rather than dependant on the behaviour. This procedure is commonly referred to as non-contingent reinforcement (NCR). For example, if the identified reinforcer for the behaviour is attention, attention will be provided to the individual on a fixed-time basis, for example every 10 minutes. If there are concerns about the attention being delivered and accidentally being paired with the behaviour, then a brief delay of delivery can be employed in such circumstances. NCR effectively weakens the relationship between the behaviour and the attention with a resulting decrease in the behaviour. This may be considered analogous to a situation whereby an employee goes to work in order to earn money. This employee wins a large sum on the lottery with the resulting effect of him no longer being motivated to go to work. The relative value of his wages have been reduced by the amount of money he now has, and this affects his motivation to work for what has now effectively become loose change.

Conclusion

- The primary goal of focused support/direct treatment strategies within LaVigna and Willis's multi-element model for supporting people with learning disabilities and challenging behaviour is to establish rapid control over the behaviour in order to reduce the associated risks.
- These risks are often those involved with reacting to the behaviour.
- The three main categories of focused support strategies are the use of differential reinforcement schedules, removal and/or altering antecedent conditions, and non-contingent reinforcement.

References

Didden R, Duker P & Korzilius H (1997) Meta-analytical study on treatment effectiveness for problem behaviours with individuals who have mental retardation. *American Journal on Mental Retardation* **101** (4) 387–399.

Donnellan A, LaVigna G, Negri-Shoultz N & Fassbender L (1988) *Progress without Punishment.* New York: Teachers College Press.

Horner RH, Day MH & Day JR (1997) Using neutralizing routines to reduce problem behaviors. *Journal of Applied Behavior Analysis* **30** 601–614.

LaVigna G & Donnellan A (1986) *Alternatives to Punishment.* New York: Irvington Publishers.

LaVigna G & Willis T (1995) Challenging behaviour: a model for breaking the barriers to social and community integration. *Positive Practices* **1** (1) 8–15.

Miltenberger RG (2006) Antecedent interventions for challenging behaviors maintained by escape from instructional activities. In: JK Luiselli (Ed) *Antecedent Assessment and Intervention: Supporting children and adults with development disabilities in community settings.* Baltimore: Brooks.

Royal College of Psychiatrists (2007) *Challenging Behaviour: A unified approach.* London: RCP.

Chapter 6

Reactive management strategies

Lisa Russell

This chapter focuses on reactive strategies and aims to provide greater insight into the purpose of a reactive strategy; common errors and misunderstandings; why we need to plan strategies; and how to devise the best possible strategy when supporting an individual who is presenting with behaviours that are considered to be challenging. It is important to remember that challenging behaviour is socially constructed and has meaning to the individual. It is a product of interactions between the individual and their environment and has a legitimate function. It is, therefore, highly likely that if challenging behaviour occurs it is an indication that we are not meeting the person's needs in some way. If we lose sight of this fact, we are in danger of seeing the behaviour and the person as the same thing.

Reactive?

What does it mean to be reactive? The term 'reactive' refers to how we respond to situations and particularly to situations that may evoke an emotional response. When considering challenging behaviour, the emotional response could be anxiety, fear, confusion, anger, or even embarrassment. For example, there may be fear of the person or the safety of the person; fear for the safety and comfort of others around the person; or fear of possible damage to the person's environment. In these situations, an individual often likes to take control, to regain 'order', and reduce any possible perceived threat.

We respond to situations by using our experiences, values, and emotions to decide what our response will be. If we rely on this method of response to challenging behaviour, it is likely that we will be 'reacting' to the situation in an inappropriate (and inconsistent) way. If we simply 'react', with no understanding of *why* an individual is doing something, or without an appropriate *plan*, the situation can escalate and even become dangerous by eliciting greater anxiety, and by not responding to the person's attempts to communicate a need to us – all behaviour has meaning. We need to understand what the person's behaviour is communicating to us so that we can respond in the most appropriate way; not doing so will increase the likelihood of punishment-based, unethical strategies being used.

Baker *et al* (1998) state that: *'Even with the most carefully designed proactive strategies, the likelihood of the occurrence of the behaviour should be carefully considered. Not to address this issue is to place both the individual and the carers at risk. Indeed, the failure to plan for dealing with the occurrence of challenging behaviour makes the use of punishment-based strategies more likely.'*

However, it must not be ignored that: *'Families who care for individuals whose behaviour presents challenges are subject to considerable and continual stress, both physical and psychological. Although staff are not permanently on duty as family carers can be, they are still subject to the same stresses when supporting people whose behaviour challenges.'* (Mansell, 2007)

Assessment of challenging behaviour

It is important that staff and families have access to the necessary professional support and provision, which will include a behavioural assessment, in seeking to gain a clear understanding of the individual, their environment, and how the individual interacts with their the environment. The aim of the assessment is to reduce challenging behaviour and to improve the quality of life for the individual, their family and support staff. An assessment aims to find out what the person is trying to say through their behaviour, and to change things in their environment (including how others respond to them) so that we can meet their needs. This does not mean 'fixing' the person – they are not broken.

A multi-element approach: The LaVigna model

Following assessment, a multi-element, multi-component intervention plan can be devised to provide a 'better fit' between the individual and their environment. The LaVigna model (LaVigna *et al,* 1989) is based on the constructional approach (building, piece by piece) and seeks to assist individuals to develop new skills and repertoires. This building of skills is commonly known as 'positive programming'. The model is a multi-element, multi-component intervention plan that is based on the principle of non-aversive techniques for the reduction of challenging behaviour. This, in the long term, is more likely to be effective in positive behavioural changes than an approach based on punishment, which simply suppresses behaviour without supplying any appropriate behaviour replacements.

The framework takes into account two main areas for intervention strategy.

1. **Proactive strategies** focus on prevention of challenging behaviour, and for bringing about positive behavioural change. These strategies are essential, but can take time to take effect.
2. **Reactive strategies** are designed to respond safely and quickly, while preserving everybody's dignity in response to challenging behaviour. They do not have the purpose of bringing about long-term behavioural change.

Reactive management strategies

Reactive strategies aim to bring the behaviour under control safely, quickly and in a non-aversive way. They are most effective when used at the very start of the behavioural chain so, for example, if the individual begins to rock, then loudly vocalise, then scream, and then break something, it is best to intervene when the person begins to rock (unless of course they happen to be rocking to music). This means understanding that the person is communicating that they have a need, and they need you to help fulfil that need – isn't that a reasonable request?

Reactive strategies are not designed to be clever. That is the role of proactive strategies (see Chapters 3, 4, 7 and 8). Reactive strategies are to be used alongside the proactive strategies, which are designed to bring about long-term environmental and behavioural change. The best way to fulfil this need is to understand what it is the person wants, and give it to them. This may seem counter intuitive with staff often thinking: 'But won't this just reinforce the behaviour?' The idea is not to teach the person that their behaviour is wrong at this moment (a legitimate need is never wrong), but to prevent the behaviour from escalating – the intended goal is a rapid, dignified resolution. For example, if you know the person wants attention, it may not be helpful to decide that 'attention seeking' is a bad thing, and ignore them – the behaviour will escalate, and then you will have to give them some attention! Isn't it the case that when you go and chat to your work colleague or friend, you are asking for their attention? Imagine how you would feel if they ignored you.

The answer to the reinforcement question is: if one of the functions of the behaviour is to gain the attention of others, then regular, predictable, quality, non-contingent attention should be built into the proactive strategies, becoming part of everyday life, along with the introduction of skills building so that the person can gain the attention of others in other ways. The need to gain the attention of others through the use of challenging behaviour will be far less likely.

Key points:

- challenging behaviour communicates a legitimate need
- it is communication
- reactive strategies are not meant to be clever; the goal is to bring about rapid resolution, using non-aversive techniques
- reactive strategies are not designed to bring about long-term behavioural change – this is the purpose of the proactive strategies.

Developing reactive strategies

Having established the purpose of non-aversive reactive strategies, there remains the issue of how to write them. Here are some suggestions.

- Whenever possible, gather together the people (staff, relatives, professionals, friends) who know the person most. Hearing from a range of people will provide a greater perspective about the person, and the circumstances in which the behaviours will and will not occur.
- Ensure that, where possible, you have looked at data such as ABC charts etc, to better inform you about the circumstances and situations in which behaviours are more likely to occur, and what things typically happen

following a behaviour ie. what comes into an individual's life or is taken away? This helps to identify what the function(s) of the behaviour may be.

- Assess the risk; this includes taking into account events in the person's life that will make typical triggers to behaviours more powerful and therefore more likely that the person may move more rapidly through the behavioural chain. For example, is the person feeling ill; did they have a good night's sleep; have they been having epileptic seizures; have other events occurred that will make the person more sensitive?
- Decide what behaviour(s), and under what circumstances, you wish to write strategies for; this needs to be clear because the same behaviour may have different functions in different settings. For example, a person may begin to rock and vocalise while sitting on a bus, and thus may mean that they want attention, whereas the same behaviour while undertaking a task may mean that the task is too difficult, or that they want a break. This one behaviour may be all that the person has at the moment in their behavioural repertoire to make their needs known. This must be identified so that the right strategy can be used under each circumstance – a very person-centred approach (and the only one that will be successful).
- Have a clear understanding of the behavioural chain and intervene at the earliest possible opportunity – don't wait until the behaviour escalates and there is a full blown, possibly dangerous, incident. This means recognising and responding to the earliest signs that the behaviour is going to occur.
- When writing your strategies, as well as taking into account the triggers and early warning signs that behaviours may occur, know details such as whether or not the person likes to be touched or not, whether they want you close to them or not, whether they like eye contact, and so on.
- Be aware of your own behaviour, such as tone of voice, body language and facial expression – rapport is so important! Don't get into power struggles – this does not take into account the person's needs and is likely to be counterproductive.
- Don't repeat instructions again and again, or have too many people giving instructions. This will not help the person to process information and will again be counterproductive.
- Think about how the written guidelines will be shared with others – to other members of the staff team and family members, and how you will monitor and evaluate the success and implementation of the guidelines, ensuring consistency.

Examples of reactive strategies

- **Strategic capitulation** means providing the person with what they want as soon as the precursor behaviour is evident. Remember that the purpose of this strategy is resolution. This method is used alongside proactive strategies. This means that the person is communicating what they want through their behaviour. It will be available to them at other times, not just when they present with challenging behaviours.
- **Avoiding natural consequences** of a behaviour for a person doesn't seem helpful to many staff, as it is widely believed that an individual will not learn from the consequences of their behaviour if staff intervene. However, LaVigna and Willis (1997) suggest that allowing a person to experience the natural consequences of their behaviour may actually escalate into a greater crisis, and lead to further devaluation and exclusion. Behaviours will have typically been occurring for many years, so if individuals have not learned by experiencing the natural consequences to behaviours already, then they are not likely to – particularly when considering those who have higher support needs.
- **Stimulus change** is the introduction of a 'novel' stimulus (event) used to interrupt the behavioural chain by introducing a 'surprise' into the environment. For example, starting a sing-a-long (one that the person knows and likes would be beneficial), along with dancing and clapping, laughing, dancing with someone else. The idea of stimulus change is to provide a novel stimulus, so don't do the same thing all the time, but have a range of planned strategies that you can use, and a plan of what you are going to do next (such as instructional control/re-direction), as this strategy may only provide you with a short window of opportunity.
- **Instructional control/redirecting** involves interrupting the behavioural chain by asking the person to do something (that they like), or to help you with an activity in another area of the building (again, something the person likes to do). Remember that when people become anxious or aroused, their ability to process information will be affected (think about how much more difficult it is for you to concentrate when you are anxious), so use pictures or objects to assist the person's understanding – don't risk escalating the behaviour by asking them to do something they don't understand.

Physical interventions

When using reactive strategies, we should always plan to use the least restrictive way to bring the behaviour under rapid control – to bring about resolution. However, sometimes, when considering severe challenging behaviour, and when all other methods have been exhausted, if the person and others remain at risk of physical harm, then physical interventions may be necessary. As with all other strategies, this must be a planned intervention, and a last resort. These interventions should not be implemented by people who are not trained to use them, and should adhere to strict guidelines by those who are trained. Not to do so could result in greater injury to the person or to others and, should unplanned strategies cause injury, result in disciplinary and/or legal action being taken against those involved. Any type of physical intervention should be planned in a multidisciplinary forum and adhere to local policy, national guidance and law (DH, 2002). It should also be available in writing, and be monitored.

Breakaway techniques

Specific training is required to undertake safe and effective breakaway techniques. This method of physical intervention is the least likely to cause injury to any party involved. The techniques are to be used by those who are being held in an aggressive or dangerous manner, resulting in swift freedom from the grip of another, using momentum, not force, to release the person's grip. Following this, strategies such as instructional control, redirection, and strategic capitulation can be used.

Physical restraint

Physical restraint is rarely used in community-based settings. This is because safe and effective (and legal) physical restraint techniques need a minimum of three trained individuals to appropriately implement this type of intervention.

Key points:

- physical interventions should be planned – never unplanned
- physical interventions should be agreed in a multidisciplinary forum
- only trained individuals should implement physical interventions
- physical interventions should be written, understood by all staff, and monitored carefully
- all guidelines should undergo regular review

- all physical interventions should adhere to local policy, national guidance and law (DH, 2002).

Conclusion

- Reactive strategies are to be used alongside proactive strategies. Remember that proactive strategies typically take time to become really effective in bringing about positive behavioural change.
- Reactive strategies are designed to bring about rapid resolution to challenging behaviour, and are not designed to bring about long-term positive behavioural change.
- All reactive strategies should be planned based upon current evidence of the function(s) of the behaviour.
- Physical interventions should be used only as a last resort, carefully planned in a multidisciplinary forum, and undertaken only by trained individuals according to strict guidelines, local policy, national guidance and law.
- Finally, remember never to get the individual and the behaviour mixed up. Look at what the person's behaviour is telling you, and meet their needs.

References

Baker P, LaVigna G & Willis T (1998) Understanding and responding to challenging behaviour: a multi-element approach. In: W Fraser, D Sines & M Kerr (Eds) *Hallas: The Care of People with Learning Disabilities.* Oxford: Butterworths.

Department of Health (2002) *Guidance on Restrictive Physical Interventions for People with Learning Disability and Autistic Spectrum Disorder, in Health, Education and Social Care Settings.* London: TSO.

La Vigna GW, Willis TTJ & Donnellan AM (1989) The role of positive programming in behavioural treatment. In: C Cipini (Ed) *The Treatment of Severe Behaviour Disorders.* Washington DC: American Association on Mental Retardation.

La Vigna GW & Willis TTJ (1997) Severe and challenging behaviour: counter-intuitive strategies for crisis management within a non-aversive framework. *Positive Practices* **2** (2).

Mansell JM (2007) *Services for People with Learning Disabilities and Challenging Behaviour or Mental Health Needs (Revised edition).* London: TSO.

Chapter 7

Cognitive approaches to challenging behaviour

Stephen C. Oathamshaw

This chapter will discuss the development of cognitive behavioural approaches to the treatment of psychological difficulties in people with learning disabilities, including challenging behaviour. People whose behaviour challenges services can sometimes access individual and group therapeutic interventions and case examples will be used to illustrate the use of this approach. Ways of adapting therapy to make it accessible to people with learning disabilities and how to assess an individual's ability to benefit from this approach will also be described. Cognitive and cognitive behavioural approaches to challenging behaviour are designed to complement other approaches used with individuals and support staff and not to replace them. Empowering individuals to develop ways of managing their own behaviour is a key aspect of this approach.

Cognitive behavioural approaches to anger management were first described in the mid-1980s, for example by Benson *et al* (1986). Anger problems are how challenging behaviour is often described in people who have mild learning disabilities and anger management continues to be recognised as the area of therapy with the most evidence to support its use (Frankish & Terry, 2003). Cognitive behavioural interventions for anger management can be delivered individually (Taylor & Novaco, 2005) or with groups (Willner *et al,* 2002) and although many of the interventions described in the literature have been delivered by psychologists, a current large-scale trial is evaluating anger-management groups run by support workers and day service staff (Willner *et al*, 2002).

Services for people with learning disabilities aim to improve individuals' quality of life in line with government policy documents and clinical guidelines, for example, *Valuing People Now* (DH, 2009); *The Same as You* by (Scottish Executive, 2000); *Challenging Behaviour: A unified approach* (Royal College of Psychiatrists *et al*, 2007). Behaviours that challenge services include behaviours that make this aim difficult to achieve; including psychological difficulties such as low mood and anxiety, symptoms of psychosis such as auditory (verbal) hallucinations and obsessive or ritualistic behaviours. These behaviours challenge as they may make the person difficult to engage in skills teaching or leisure activities and to support to access community resources.

Cognitive behavioural approaches have also been shown to be effective with depression and low mood (McGillivray *et al,* 2007), anxiety difficulties (Douglass *et al,* 2007), symptoms of psychosis (Haddock *et al*, 2004) and obsessive behaviours (Willner & Goodey, 2006). People with autism often display behaviours that challenge services and cognitive behavioural approaches have also been shown to be effective with some people with autism (Hare, 1997). Sexually inappropriate behaviours and sexual offending can also present a significant challenge to services and cognitive behavioural therapy interventions have been shown to be effective with individuals who have these behaviours (Lindsay & Smith, 1998).

Cognitive behavioural therapy (CBT)

CBT is what is known as a 'talking therapy', which means it is only suitable for people with learning disabilities who are able to use speech to communicate, or have a well-developed alternative communication system such as British Sign Language (BSL). Some CBT interventions, particularly behavioural interventions, can be used with people who have less developed verbal communication, but this therapy approach is not suitable for people with more severe learning disabilities who may have no verbal communication. There are some assessments available for assessing an individual's ability to engage in a CBT approach, but communication assessment conducted by a speech and language therapist should always be considered if it is available.

CBT is based on two basic principles. First, the principle that what we think and feel affects our behaviour and second, that if we change how we think about a situation it can change how we feel and behave. An example may be that if a person thinks they sound stupid when they try and talk to other people in a social situation (thought), they will feel anxious whenever social situations arise (feeling) and will avoid these situations whenever possible (behaviour). The goal of work conducted during therapy and outside therapy during real-life situations would be to develop more positive thoughts such as 'everybody says the wrong thing sometimes' and 'saying the wrong thing doesn't mean people think I'm stupid or a bad person'. Examples of how these changes can be achieved will be described later in this chapter.

Assessing ability to engage in CBT

Since benefiting from CBT requires the cognitive ability to recognise how different situations will make us think, feel and behave, assessments have been developed to assess the skills that people with learning disabilities have to recognise these links and areas where they may need to develop cognitive skills further. Reed and Clements (1989) described an assessment for identifying if someone could make an appropriate link between a situation and a simple emotional response (happy or sad). The ability to make links between events and emotions is a prerequisite for CBT, but does not include thoughts – an essential component of this approach. Oathamshaw and Haddock (2006) developed a method of assessing how good someone was at recognising and differentiating behaviours, thoughts and feelings. This assessment does not consider if someone can recognise how behaviours, thoughts and feelings are linked, but will identify if they are confused about which component is which. The assessment developed by Dagnan and Chadwick (1997) identifies if someone can make appropriate links between situations, feelings and thoughts, and considers the central component of CBT; how thoughts affect, or mediate, feelings and behaviour.

In addition to considering the cognitive skills necessary to participate in and benefit from CBT, it is necessary to consider other factors that may improve the likelihood of success, or present barriers. Motivation to engage in therapy is key to success as CBT is an approach where the therapist and participant work together towards an agreed goal, but the participant must be committed to practice techniques and implement strategies outside therapy sessions. One factor that can affect motivation is the person's belief in their own ability to achieve change; this is what is known as 'self-efficacy'. Many people with learning disabilities are used to having changes in their lives managed or initiated by carers or staff, and the early stages of CBT are often about supporting people to recognise they can make changes to improve their quality of life themselves and need to take responsibility for making changes happen.

This is not to suggest that people with learning disabilities are expected to achieve changes designed to improve their psychological well-being and quality of life on their own. Many people with learning disabilities receive support from carers and staff and the support available to achieve positive behavioural change is often crucial to its chances of success and to ensuring positive change continues after therapy has been completed. Environmental factors such as the person's relationships with staff and people they live with and access to resources can also be crucial to the chances of successful therapy. Stenfert Kroese (1997) has discussed the difficulties of conducting CBT with individuals who live in an unpleasant or even abusive environment, and Oathamshaw (2007) describes an example of therapy for anger problems that is undermined by environmental difficulties and a lack of positive support.

Adapting CBT for people with learning disabilities

As CBT is a talking therapy, many of the interventions are verbally based, but can be easily adapted to be more accessible to people with learning disabilities. CBT also essentially includes the use of 'homework' or work done outside therapy to reinforce techniques learnt during therapy sessions, or practice interventions to achieve further learning. An example of this would be a homework task for a person who often got angry when his housemate shouted at the staff. A behavioural recording sheet would be completed during the therapy session detailing how he thought in these situations ('he's trying to wind me up'), felt (angry) and behaved (started shouting at his housemate), and how he may think, feel and behave differently, resulting in a different outcome. The success, or not, of this alternative way of handling his housemate's behaviour would be reviewed in the next session. This way of working is often more effective for people with learning disabilities as it creates opportunities for reinforcing learning outside therapy sessions.

Other ways of adapting therapy include the use of pictures and symbols, simplified visual rating scales rather than numerical, recording forms to be used at home (for example, ABC sheets for detailing anger episodes, although in this context the A is the activating event, B – thoughts, C – feelings and behaviours) with simple language supported by line drawings or symbols. The anger-management programme developed by Taylor and Novaco (2005) contains examples of this sort of recording sheet. The internet can also be an invaluable source of downloadable pictures and symbols that can be used to increase understanding during therapy and ability to implement agreed interventions at home. Therapy letters are often used in other psychological therapies (for example, cognitive analytic therapy). With people who have learning disabilities, a therapy book developed during sessions and given to the person at the end of therapy can be invaluable. Therapy books can contain strategies, techniques and helpful thoughts learned and practised during therapy, and provide a structured reminder so progress during therapy can be maintained and further developed.

Many of the adaptations described above mean therapy with people who have learning disabilities has a slower pace, takes longer, and incorporates opportunities for repetition and multiple practice of strategies learned outside the therapy sessions.

Staff can also play an important role in increasing the chances of CBT being successful and of positive changes being continued after therapy has been completed. This is one of the key differences between CBT practised in adult mental health settings, where often the therapist and client will meet on a one-to-one basis for an agreed course of therapy and no one else is involved, and the learning disability setting where most clients receive support from staff or carers on a visiting or 24-hour basis. Particularly in group therapy, staff may attend sessions or be available if the person needs a break. For individual therapy, staff are often briefed on what has been covered during a session so that they can support the person with a learning disability to practice strategies (for example, relaxation, or different ways of reacting in an anger-provoking situation) or complete agreed homework such as recording sheets, if required. They may also be asked to support the person to carry out a behavioural experiment appropriately, without giving the person so much support that their belief they cannot do it on their own (for example) is reinforced.

Case study: Sharon

This case example is fictionalised but is based on therapy conducted by the author and his colleagues.

Sharon was a thirty-eight-year-old woman with a mild learning disability. She had suffered from anxiety for most of her life and her mum and dad, with whom she lived until moving into supported living at the age of 30, were also anxious. Sharon was fearful of visiting shopping centres and would only go with a staff member. She had recently started to experience anxiety attacks at home, making her reluctant to participate in cooking, something she had previously enjoyed. An assessment found she was able to make links between situations and how she felt and behaved, and was able to describe some thoughts she had in real-life situations when she experienced anxiety.

The therapist worked with Sharon to develop a history, or timeline, of her life and how her anxiety had worsened since she was a young woman. There were no key events identified, however Sharon had gradually become anxious about more situations and progressively lost confidence to cope with activities she had previously enjoyed as her life became more restricted. Sharon had a belief she was incompetent, having often been told she was stupid at school, and when facing an anxiety-provoking situation had thoughts like: 'I can't do this' and 'everyone's looking at me because they think I'm stupid'.

The assessment information was drawn together into a 'formulation' or explanatory framework that was shared with Sharon to illustrate how her anxiety difficulties were being maintained by her increasing avoidance of anxiety-provoking situations and the best way to address this was to start, with the support of staff, to put herself back into these situations, allowing her anxiety to reduce as she learned she could cope. This strategy of graduated exposure is based on the core behavioural principle of 'habituation', where exposure to a fear (or highly enjoyable stimulus) results in a reduction of arousal (positive or negative) allowing, or in the case of a positive stimulus requiring, repeated and greater exposure. Protective factors identified included Sharon's positive relationships with staff and several relatives who lived nearby.

Case study: Sharon (continued)

Intervention included the use of a behavioural hierarchy, rating feared situations ranging from Sharon's least feared – the local shop with a trusted member of staff – to her most feared – the out-of-town supermarket on her own. Staff had a key role, both in supporting Sharon to expose herself to the increasingly feared situations, but also because Sharon had previously sought lots of reassurance from them, meaning she did not learn she could cope with these situations on her own. The therapist also worked with the staff team in helping them to support Sharon during the exposure programme, but without providing excessive reassurance. The therapist and Sharon developed a scale for monitoring her level of anxiety during each shop visit.

Other interventions included canvassing opinions among the staff and others to identify whether other people ever felt nervous about going into busy, unfamiliar environments, or thought people ever looked at them thinking they looked stupid. The results from this 'survey' were shared with Sharon, demonstrating others also sometimes experienced these thoughts. This information surprised Sharon as she thought other people didn't think like that and it was used to question her negative beliefs, which underpinned her anxious feelings. Other behavioural approaches included the introduction of a relaxation programme at home, again supported by staff, and a list of activities Sharon could try when feeling anxious such as listening to her favourite music, or having a bath with aromatic bath oils.

The therapist worked with Sharon until she had made significant progress accessing feared environments. As anticipated, her anxiety reduced and her negative thoughts in these situations were increasingly replaced with thoughts like 'I can do this'. A therapy book was produced with Sharon and a final meeting with her and the staff team was used to ensure everyone understood what more was needed to help Sharon continue to progress. A follow-up session with Sharon three months later found she had continued to visit larger shops with minimal staff support and the final feared environment (the out-of-town supermarket) was next on the list.

This chapter has discussed the small but growing evidence base that shows that adapted CBT can be effective with people who have learning disabilities and whose behaviour challenges services. Ways of assessing someone's ability to access CBT were detailed and a range of methods for adapting therapy to make it accessible for people who have learning disabilities were illustrated.

As with other approaches to people whose behaviour challenges services, a key aim of adapted CBT is to improve a person's quality of life, in this case by empowering people to learn ways of managing their psychological difficulties more effectively, thus allowing them to access environments and activities that enrich their lives. The examples discussed and the case study demonstrates that the success of individual CBT can be very reliant on support from staff and support workers can play a crucial role with this approach, as with other interventions, to support people whose behaviour is challenging more effectively.

Conclusion

- There is now a small evidence base that a therapy with considerable evidence of effectiveness for people with mental health problems can also be effective with people who have learning disabilities and whose behaviour challenges services.
- To be effective with the people we support, CBT has to be adapted to take into account people's cognitive difficulties. This chapter has discussed such adaptations.
- Support workers can be crucially important in helping with CBT interventions and supporting individuals to benefit from therapy.
- With these adaptations and support, people with learning disabilities can be empowered to manage their psychological difficulties more effectively and improve their quality of life.

References

Benson BA, Rice CJ & Miranti SV (1986) Effects of anger management training with mentally retarded adults in group treatment. *Journal of Consulting and Clinical Psychology* **54** 728–729.

Dagnan D & Chadwick P (1997) Cognitive-behaviour therapy for people with learning disabilities: assessment and intervention. In: B Stenfert Kroese, D Dagnan and K Loumidis (Eds) *Cognitive Behaviour Therapy for People with Learning Disabilities.* London: Routledge.

Department of Health (2009) *Valuing People Now.* London: TSO.

Douglass S, Palmer K & O'Connor C (2007) Experiences of running an anxiety management group for people with a learning disability using a cognitive behavioural intervention. *British Journal of Learning Disabilities* **35** 245–252.

Frankish P & Terry S (2003) Modern therapeutic approaches in learning disability services. *Tizard Learning Disability Review* **8** 3–10.

Hare DJ (1997) The use of cognitive-behavioural therapy with people with Asperger syndrome: a case study. *Autism* **1** 215–225.

Haddock G, Lobban F, Hatton C & Carson R (2004) Cognitive behaviour therapy for people with psychosis and mild learning disabilities: a case series. *Clinical Psychology and Psychotherapy* **11** 282–298.

Lindsay WR & Smith AHW (1998) Responses to treatment for sex offenders with learning disability. *Journal of Learning Disability Research* **42** 346–353.

McGillivray J, McCabe M & Kershaw M (2007) Depression in people with learning disability: An evaluation of a staff-administered treatment program. *Research in Developmental Disabilities* **29** 24–536.

Oathamshaw SC & Haddock G (2006) Do people with learning disabilities and psychosis have the cognitive skills required to undertake cognitive behavioural therapy? *Journal of Applied Research in Learning Disabilities* **19** 35–46.

Oathamshaw SC (2007) Delivering cognitive behavioural therapy in community services for people with learning disabilities: difficulties, dilemmas, confounds. *Advances in Mental Health and Learning Disabilities* **1** (2) 22–25.

Reed J & Clements J (1989) Assessing the understanding of emotional states in a population of adolescents and young adults with mental handicaps. *Journal of Mental Deficiency Research* **33** 229–233.

Royal College of Psychiatrists, British Psychological Society and Royal College of Speech and Language Therapists (2007) *Challenging Behaviour: A unified approach. College Report CR144.* London: RCPsych.

Stenfert Kroese B (1997) Cognitive-behaviour therapy for people with learning disabilities: Conceptual and contextual issues. In B Stenfert Kroese, D Dagnan and K Loumidis (Eds) *Cognitive-Behaviour Therapy for People with Learning Disabilities.* London: Routledge.

Taylor JL & Novaco RW (2005) *Anger Treatment for People with Developmental Disabilities.* Chichester: John Wiley & Sons Ltd.

Scottish Executive (2000) *The Same as You.* Edinburgh: The Scottish Executive.

Willner P & Goodey R (2006) Interaction of cognitive distortions and cognitive treatment in the formulation and treatment of obesessive-compulsive behaviours in a woman with a learning disability. *Journal of Applied Research in Learning Disabilities* **19** (1) 67–73.

Willner P, Jones J, Tams R & Green G (2002) A randomized controlled trial of the efficacy of a cognitive-behavioural anger management group for clients with learning disabilities. *Journal of Applied Research in Learning Disabilities* **15** 224–235.

Chapter 8

Developing skills

Jo Dwyer and Cleia Hayashi

'Each person wants to participate effectively in life and to remain healthy and happy. To achieve these goals a person needs a degree of personal competence in a range of culturally accepted, useful and meaningful occupations.' Duncan (2006)

Duncan (2006) suggests that people want to participate effectively in their life and that if they are able to do this satisfactorily they will achieve a better sense of health and well-being. There is no reason to assume that this is not also true for people with learning disabilities, including those whose behaviour is described as challenging.

Given the commonly held view of challenging behaviour as a socially constructed concept – in part as a consequence of the interactions between a person and their environment (DH, 2007; Royal College of Psychiatrists *et al,* 2007) – it is surely important to consider how well a person is supported to interact in their environment and the degree to which their environment offers them opportunities to maintain and develop a good quality of life. The ability to support participation and engagement in a person's environment is thus an important skill to be developed by those who support people whose behaviour is described as challenging.

A cultural challenge

'Each individual should have the support and opportunity to be the person he or she wants to be.' (DH, 2001)

Following the publication of *Valuing People* (2001), the principles of rights, independence, choice and inclusion have been paramount in many of the services working for and with people with learning disabilities. Mansell

(DH, 2007) comments that the difficulties in embedding these principles is evident in the lives of people with learning disabilities whose behaviour is described as challenging. The challenge is to embrace these principles for all people with learning disabilities to enable them to lead fulfilling lives.

However, despite current legislation promoting the view that people with learning disabilities have the right to participate equally in society (DH, 2009), in reality people with learning disabilities often experience a lack of opportunity in involvement in everyday activities. This might be because they do not have experience of being involved in activities in the past, have difficulty expressing themselves and communicating their needs and wishes, but it might also be due to cultural expectations.

The views attached to having learning disabilities will be different in different environments, depending on the cultural influences of that environment. For example, a culture that views the person with learning disabilities as 'a perpetual child' will view that person as being unable to take on adult roles.

Those who also have a label of 'challenging behaviour' are often afforded little opportunity to participate in their environment or engage in activities that promote independence or integration. Mansell (DH, 2007) reports that evidence shows the support received by those whose behaviour is described as challenging averages at around nine minutes of support in every hour and only up to four minutes in an hour of support to engage in their environment. Mansell also identifies that behaviours can arise and persist in accordance with the person's environment and the opportunities available within it. It follows then that if a person's environment affords them opportunities for participation and positive engagement, then challenging behaviours may not endure.

It is important to develop a culture within organisations that understands a person's strengths and limitations and supports them to participate in their life in accordance with their own individual needs and wishes.

The benefits of engagement

'Given a choice between always being helped to do something or being able to do it independently, most people would choose the latter because of the freedom it brings (freedom from needing other people, freedom to choose when and how to do it).' (Mansell *et al,* 1987)

People get excited when engaging in activities that they enjoy and when they are learning new skills. Csikszentmihaly (1992, cited in Goodman *et al*, 2009) describes that when a person is actively involved in an activity they become unaware of the passing of time. This phenomenon has been linked to happiness – *'time flies when you're having fun!'*

Taking on roles within a person's environment promotes a sense of value and importance. This can gain respect and put people with learning disabilities on a more equal footing with others. Being involved in a variety of activities will offer a wide range of experiences and increases interactions with others. This will all impact positively on a person's quality of life.

Boredom and a lack of involvement in activities can impact negatively on people, including those with learning disabilities. Boredom can result not only from not having activities to engage in, but also from engaging in activities that lack meaning and importance to a person. The meaningfulness of an activity is unique to each individual and so each person should be supported to explore and engage in activities that offer them meaning.

Selecting activities

The challenge for services and those supporting people with learning disabilities is to maximise people's potential and ensure a good quality of life in line with the individual needs and preferences of that person.

Whether your aim is to develop a person's skills through systematic teaching or to simply increase a person's opportunity to be involved, the choice of the activity is key. When deciding upon what activities should be offered to a person, consider what their preference would be. Think about what the person likes to do now and what they have enjoyed in the past. Think about who knows the person well and who might be able to provide ideas on possible activity choices.

Think about the activity:

- Is it something the person wants to do?
- Is it socially acceptable?
- Is it dignified?

- Is it age-appropriate?
- Does it impact positively or negatively on the lives of others?
- Is it meaningful for the person?
- Does it promote independence and self-esteem?
- Will it be a positive experience for the person with learning disabilities to be part of?
- Is it achievable?
- Are there the resources in place to support it? (For example, staff, time, finances physical environment.)

(Goodman *et al,* 2009)

Risk assessment will form an important part of this too and risks should be carefully considered. While considering risk we should remember that we all take risks in life and services should not be averse to positive risk taking in order to improve a person's quality of life.

Promoting participation

It is not always the aim for a person to be independent in an activity, sometimes the aim is to be involved. In this instance the supporter's role is to do an activity *with* the person with learning disabilities, rather than for them. When a supporter does something for a person with learning disabilities they may have removed an opportunity for the person with learning disabilities to play an active role in their environment.

When supporting a person to participate it is important that the supporter maintains their attention to the person and the task. The provision of attention contingent on engagement has been shown to increase activity levels in people with learning disabilities.

It is important that services consider what opportunities there are to promote participation. This will include regularly occurring routine activities as well as optional ones (often linked to an individual's personal preferences). It is also important that services monitor the opportunities that are provided each day. This monitoring will help to increase staff awareness of their routines and the opportunities available to the people they support, with the aim of increasing staff performance.

Staff working with people with learning disabilities will often have the role of promoting participation and involvement written into their job descriptions.

Teaching skills

For some people with learning disabilities the aim of engaging them in an activity will be to develop their competence and independence. It is important that the activity choice is realistic and repeated regularly and consistently so that the person has the maximum opportunity to learn the required skills. The aim of skills teaching is for the person to learn part or all of a new skill. It is important to choose an achievable and appropriate task in accordance with the person's strengths and needs. Once an activity has been selected the next step will be to consider how to develop a skills teaching programme around the activity.

The person supporting the skills teaching programme should have a trusting relationship with the person with learning disabilities and have a positive attitude towards the programme. It is important for the person supporting the programme to have tried it out beforehand before supporting the person with learning disabilities to carry out the task, so that they are familiar with each stage of the activity, the risk areas (if any), and the steps where support might be required. The overall aims of the programme should be clear so that the expected outcome of the programme is clear and the steps to achieving the outcome are realistically set. The person's strengths and needs (including their cultural needs) will influence how the programme is planned and presented.

Understanding the activity will help the person teaching to determine exactly what needs to be taught and how. It will help the person teaching to identify and organise a routine in a logical way to enable the development of the programme.

Considerations for the person teaching include:

- how the skill will be taught
- when the skill will be taught
- where the skill will be taught

- how the programme will be monitored
- what is a realistic timetable to teach the skill and when the programme should be reviewed
- the environment in which the activity will be taught.

It is easy to make assumptions about a person's ability before they try an activity. When breaking down the activity into steps, a baseline is established. If difficulties arise it is easier to identify where exactly the problem is by considering the various steps of the activity, and it is possible then to make specific adjustments to the training steps.

Before starting the activity it is important that the environment has been prepared to support the skills teaching programme:

- ensure the time and place matches the activity, for example making lunch in the kitchen at 12pm, and not in the lounge at 10am
- ensure that the person is familiar with the environment
- ensure that all the required tools are available and in working order
- limit unnecessary distractions, for example turn off the television and ask others not to interrupt.

When finalising the programme, ensure that the support given is consistent. This includes instruction and types of prompts. All those carrying out the task with the person with learning disabilities will need to follow the format that has been agreed.

It is important only to give instruction when required. If the person with learning disabilities does something incorrectly it should be corrected at the time the error occurs. The person supporting the programme should avoid saying 'no' and instead use phrases such as 'try another way'. This will help to keep the experience positive.

If the activity has been chosen well, based on the person's strengths and needs, likes and dislikes, and has been broken down to identify correctly the type of support the person needs, completion of the activity will form its own reward.

It is important to offer regular opportunities for the person with learning disabilities to practice the skill and to monitor the skills teaching programme. The programme will need to be changed if the person with learning disabilities does not appear to be developing the target skills as agreed before the programme commenced. If the person with learning disabilities develops the target skills the programme will be completed and opportunities might be sought to further develop skills.

The importance of monitoring should not be forgotten. The aim of monitoring is to provide an objective view of what is actually happening, note the progress made over time and be able to pinpoint stages of the activity that need to change. This will motivate staff and the client to continue with the activity and provide evidence to managers and commissioners that what you are doing is working.

Everyone can develop skills and the challenge for services and those supporting people with learning disabilities is to identify the right activity and opportunities for learning to occur.

Conclusion

- People with learning disabilities (including those who display behaviours described as challenging) have the right to participate effectively in their lives.
- Providing opportunities for people with learning disabilities (including those who display behaviours described as challenging) to engage in activities promotes a sense of value, enjoyment, self-esteem and general well-being.
- Providing opportunities for people with learning disabilities (including those who display behaviours described as challenging) to learn new skills enables people to be active participants in their environments. This in turn can promote competence, independence and enable people to take on new roles within their life and learn new behaviours.
- Those supporting people with learning disabilities (including those who display behaviours described as challenging) to increase their levels of participation and engagement will need to take an active role in the identification and planning of suitable activities and opportunities.

References

Csikszentmihaly M (1992) Flow: the psychology of happiness. In: J Goodman, J Hurst & C Locke (2009) *Occupational Therapy for People with Learning Disabilities: A practical guide.* London: Elsevier.

Department of Health (2001) *Valuing People: A new strategy for learning disabilities for the 21st century.* London: TSO.

Department of Health (2007) *Mansell Report: Services for people with learning disabilities and challenging behaviour or mental health needs* (revised edition). London: HMSO.

Department of Health (2009) *Valuing People Now: A new three year strategy for people with learning disabilities.* London: TSO.

Duncan EAS (2006) *Foundations for Practice in Occupational Therapy.* London: Churchill Livingstone.

Goodman J, Hurst J & Locke C (2009) *Occupational Therapy for People with Learning Disabilities: A practical guide.* London: Elsevier.

Mansell J, Felce D, Jenkins J, de Kock U & Toogood A (1987) *Developing Staffed Housing for People with Mental Handicaps.* Tunbridge Wells: Costello.

Royal College of Psychiatrists, British Psychological Society and Royal College of Speech and Language Therapists (2007) *Challenging Behaviour: A unified approach.* London: Royal College of Psychiatrists.

Chapter 9

Medication for the management of challenging behaviours in people with learning disabilities

Shoumitro Deb

There are many reasons why people with learning disabilities show behaviours that challenge (Deb *et al,* 2009). These include biological factors such as genetic disorders and psychiatric disorders, psychological factors such as cognitive impairment, and social factors such as environment and a lack of meaningful day activities. Therefore, the management of these behaviours also include a multi-factorial approach including medication-based and non medication-based treatment. Medications that are used to manage these behaviours are collectively known as psychotropic medications and were originally used for the treatment of various psychiatric disorders. Psychotropic medications used in the management of behaviours that challenge in people with learning disabilities include antipsychotics (neuroleptics), antidepressants, mood stabilisers, anti-anxiety medication, psychostimulants, opioid antagonists and beta blockers etc.

Antipsychotics

Antipsychotic medications are primarily used to treat psychoses such as schizophrenia and also mania and hypomania. Older (typical) antipsychotic medications include haloperidol and chlorpromazine. However, these medications may have serious adverse effects such as extrapyramidal symptoms that include acute dystonia (sudden abnormal posture of the body), Parkinsonian symptoms such as stiffness, tremor, akathisia (internal and external agitation), and tardive dyskinesia (long-term adverse effect with abnormal face and body movements characterised by chewing and sucking movements, grimacing, and slow turning movement of the head and limbs), also dry mouth, blurred vision and constipation.

Antipsychotic medications can worsen seizures if the individual has epilepsy or induce epileptic seizures in individuals who did not have epilepsy before. Other adverse effects are cardiac (abnormal heart rhythm such as prolonged QT interval) and sexual dysfunction (impotence, lack of libido etc), and metabolic such as raised prolactin levels. One serious adverse effect is neuroleptic malignant syndrome (NMS). This is a very rare but potentially fatal adverse effect characterised by high temperature, muscle rigidity, labile blood pressure and fluctuating levels of consciousness. It can be treated but requires hospitalisation.

Newer (atypical) antipsychotics are risperidone, olanzapine, quetiapine, clozapine, aripiprazole, paliperidone, amisulpride, zotepine and sertindole (restricted use in the UK). Possible adverse effects are extrapyramidal symptoms, metabolic syndrome, such as glucose intolerance (leading to diabetes mellitus), and weight gain. Other adverse effects are drowsiness, blood abnormalities such as agranulocytosis (particularly associated with clozapine), and sexual dysfunction. Other metabolic abnormalities include raised cholesterol and prolactin. Therefore, regular blood tests and possibly ECG are necessary to check for these adverse effects. Antipsychotic medications are usually taken orally (tablets or liquid or sometimes in dispersible form), however, it can be given as an injection to those who are unreliable or have difficulty taking oral medication.

Scientific evidence based on randomised controlled trails on children with learning disabilities (with or without autism) show that risperidone is effective in the management of behaviours that challenge (Deb, 2007; Deb & Unwin, 2007). The evidence for adults is equivocal (Deb *et al,* 2007). One study showed that a placebo was as effective as risperidone and haloperidol (Tyrer *et al*, 2008). Although there is concern about adverse effects such as excessive daytime sleepiness and weight gain, long-term follow-up studies among children show that most children are either not affected by adverse effects or that they tolerate them.

Antidepressants

Antidepressants are primarily used for the treatment of depression. For the treatment of depression it is necessary to take this medication for a couple of weeks before any effects can be seen and the treatment may need to be continued for at least six months. Antidepressants can also be used to treat generalised anxiety disorder (GAD), social anxiety, obsessive compulsive disorder (OCD) and post-traumatic stress disorder (PTSD). People with learning disabilities can be suffering from depressive symptoms and may express this outwardly by exhibiting behaviours that challenge. The older generation antidepressants are amitriptyline, clomipramine and imipramine etc. Possible adverse effects are dry mouth, constipation, blurred vision, low blood pressure, heart failure and fatality associated with overdose.

New generation antidepressants are selective serotonin reuptake inhibitors (SSRIs) such as fluoxetine, fluvoxamine, sertraline, citalopram, escitalopram, paroxetine, venlafaxine and duloxetine, which are selective nor-adrenaline reuptake inhibitors (SNRIs). Other antidepressants include mirtazapine, flupentixol, reboxetine and tryptophan. Possible adverse effects of these medications are agitation, sleep problems, sexual dysfunction, problems with withdrawal and serotonin syndrome (associated with SSRIs). The evidence in support of antidepressants' efficacy in the management of behaviours that challenge is equivocal and primarily based on prospective and retrospective case studies (Sohanpal *et al,* 2007). On average, less than half of the individuals studied showed improvement in behaviour. The rest either did not improve or deteriorated. The most pronounced effect on behaviour is shown when the individual has anxiety/depressive or OCD symptoms. However, most studies showed concern about adverse effects, which could sometimes make behaviour worse.

Mood stabilisers

Mood stabilisers are primarily used for the treatment of mania and hypomania (bipolar affective disorder). Mood stabilisers include lithium and some antiepileptic medications such as sodium valproate and carbamazepine. Lithium can also be given to help with recurrent depressive illnesses that have proved difficult to treat. For people with learning disabilities, lithium is used to help manage problem behaviours especially if the behaviours fluctuate in frequency with a fluctuating mood. Lithium's blood levels need close monitoring to help prevent serious complications that can occur. Possible adverse effects from lithium are tremor, swelling of feet, excess thirst and frequent passing of urine, kidney failure, and thyroid dysfunction. However, there is very narrow margin between lithium's therapeutic blood level and its toxic level, hence regular monitoring is very important. Lithium toxicity can cause confusion and lead to death. Common investigations that are necessary are: blood lithium level (in order to adjust the dose and prevent toxicity), full blood count (FBC), kidney function and thyroid function test (TFT).

Antiepileptic medication

Carbamazepine (Tegretol) is used to treat epilepsy. It is the drug of choice for simple and complex partial seizures and for tonic–clonic seizures secondary to focal discharge. It should be started at a low dose and gradually built up. Possible adverse effects of carbamazepine are drowsiness, double vision, ataxia (problems with balance), hyponatraemia (low blood sodium levels) and skin rash (may lead to Stevens-Johnson syndrome, which is a serious condition). Sodium valproate (Epilim) is another antiepileptic medication that is licensed for the treatment of epilepsy. Again, starting doses should be low and then gradually increased over time to help minimise adverse effects. Possible adverse effects of sodium valproate are drowsiness, weight gain, hair loss, skin rash, ataxia and in rare cases, liver function failure. Teratogenecity (abnormalities in foetus) should be kept in mind if used in women of child-bearing age. Evidence for the effectiveness of mood stabilisers in the treatment of behaviour is based on small case studies rather than a randomised control trial (Deb *et al,* 2008).

Other medications to manage behaviour

There are other medications that can be used to treat behaviours although their use is less evidence-based. These medications include anti-anxiety drugs (benzodiazepines such as diazepam and lorazepam; and buspirone), opioid antagonists (naloxone, naltrexone), psychostimulants (used for children with attention deficit hyperactivity disorder (ADHD)) such as dexamphetamine, atomoxetine, methylphenidate, beta blockers (propranolol, atenolol) etc.

The following are some examples of when medication could be considered for the management of behaviour:

1. the behaviour causes a major risk, harm and/or distress to the person or others, or to property, or any other potential severe consequences of the behaviour

2. failure of other non medicinal interventions
3. success of medicinal intervention before
4. underlying mental disorders such as anxiety, autism, ADHD etc.
5. as an adjunct to other measures; sometimes the person with learning disabilities or their carers may choose to have medication as a treatment option. In those cases a full discussion is necessary with the individual and other relevant professionals.

Assessment and formulation

Any treatment, including the use of medications, should depend on a comprehensive, holistic, person-centred assessment of the cause and effect of the behaviour, which should lead to a formulation and rationale for the use of the proposed treatment, including use of medication (Unwin & Deb, 2008). It is important to include the person (where possible) and/or their carers from the outset in the decision about using medication. Where possible, it is good practice to involve members of a multidisciplinary team such as a community learning disability team. Once prescribed it is important to monitor the outcome of the treatment and any adverse effects using standardised outcome measures. It is essential to assess the person's capacity to give consent to the treatment at the outset and if they do not have capacity, medication should only be used if it is deemed necessary in the person's best interests. However, it is important to keep in mind that the person with learning disabilities may need help with their communication so information about treatment should be presented in a form that they can understand. Medications should only be used while it is legally permitted. While assessing the outcome of the treatment, it is important also to assess the individual's and carers' quality of life.

Assessment and formulation should include identification of the behaviours that are challenging, their causes and consequences. The likes and dislikes of the person and their strengths and needs should be explored using a person-centred assessment approach. Medical factors such as an underlying medical problem, pain in the body, physical discomfort/disabilities and psychiatric disorders should be explored as possible causes of the behaviour, and treated accordingly. Psychological factors such as the person's emotional make up and cognitive impairment should be taken into account when formulating treatment options. Social factors such as overcrowded environment, lack of meaningful day and leisure activities etc should be addressed before considering any medication use. Predisposing (for example, genetic disorders), precipitating (for example, stressful life events) and perpetuating (for example, lack of appropriate care support) risk factors should be assessed and taken into account, and a full assessment of risk to the person and others should be implemented. Before considering use of medication, all other management options should be considered. The rationale for the use of medications, the desired and non-desired effects of the interventions should be considered at the outset, and monitored on a regular basis. A treatment plan should be part of an overall person-centred plan. At regular intervals, the possibility of withdrawing medications and the use of alternate methods of management should be considered.

Administering medication

People administering the medication should have basic knowledge of the purpose of the medication, the medication group, common and serious adverse effects and the action necessary to deal with them, and of any contraindication for not using the medication for the particular person. People administering the medication should check that the medication is administered at the correct time of the day (also in relation to mealtimes). The sequence for giving several medications should always be appropriate. The right dose of medication must always be administered. If in doubt, people should always check the instruction given by the prescriber or check with another staff member or the British National Formulary (BNF) (ARC, 2011)

Communication with the prescriber is very important, particularly if any changes to dosage have been made. All those involved in administering medication should be up to date with any recent changes in the dose. Recent loss or gain in weight, possible allergies, and the correct measurement for liquid formula should always be taken into account. People should be absolutely sure about the route of administration of medication, and of any changes in the instruction for that before administering it. People should have the right training before administering any medication (for example, administration of rectal diazepam or buccal midazolam). People should ensure that they have the right level of competence to administer medication. They should always ensure that the correct and safe instruments are used. The right person should be monitored after taking the medication to ensure that they do not spit it out or develop any adverse effects. All records should be kept in line with policy, regulations and best practice. The records should be legible and written in an understandable way. The records should be kept confidential and up to date, and monitored regularly. Accessible versions of information leaflets on psychotropic medications with accompanying audio versions are available for free to download from www.ld-medication.bham.ac.uk.

The use of medication for the management of behaviours that challenge in people with learning disabilities may have to be considered under certain circumstances but they should only be used if the behaviour poses a major risk and other ways of managing behaviours have not been successful. Medication should only be used after a comprehensive, person-centred assessment of the causes and effects of behaviours, and a formulation that describes the rational for its use. The outcome and adverse effects should be monitored at regular intervals and withdrawal of medication and use of non medication-based management should also be considered at regular intervals (Unwin & Deb, 2010).

Conclusion

- Medication should only be used after considering all other options for managing behaviours that challenge in people with learning disabilities.
- A comprehensive person-centred assessment followed by a formulation is necessary before considering the use of medication.
- The effect of medications and their adverse effects should be monitored at regular intervals.
- Withdrawal of medication and use of non-medication-based management of behaviour should be considered at regular intervals.
- The person with learning disabilities and their carer(s) should be fully involved in the decision-making process at all stages.
- Where possible, involve a multidisciplinary team in the decision-making process.
- Treatment plans should be part of a comprehensive person-centred plan.

References

Association for Real Change (2011) Handling medication in social care settings [online]. Available at: http://arcuk.org.uk/publications/handling-medication-in-social-care-settings (accessed 6 July 2011).

Deb S (2007) The role of medication in the management of behaviour problems in people with learning disabilities. *Advances in Mental Health and Learning Disabilities* **1** (2) 26–31.

Deb S, Sohanpal SK, Soni R, Unwin G & Lenôtre L (2007) The effectiveness of antipsychotic medication in the management of behaviour problems in adults with learning disabilities. *Journal of Learning Disability Research* **51** (10) 766–777.

Deb S & Unwin G (2007) Psychotropic medication for behaviour problems in people with learning disability: a review of the current literature. *Current Opinion in Psychiatry* **20** 461–466.

Deb S, Chaplin R, Sohanpal S, Unwin G, Soni R & Lenôtre L (2008) The effectiveness of mood stabilisers and antiepileptic medication for the management of behaviour problems in adults with learning disability: a systematic review. *Journal of Learning Disability Research* **52** (2) 107–113.

Deb S, Kwok H, Bertelli M, Salvador-Carulla L, Bradley E, Torr J & Barnhill J (2009) International guide to prescribing psychotropic medication for the management of problem behaviours in adults with learning disabilities. *World Psychiatry* **8** (3) 181–186.

Sohanpal SK, Deb S, Thomas C, Soni R, Lenôtre L & Unwin G (2007) The effectiveness of antidepressant medication in the management of behaviour problems in adults with learning disabilities: a systematic review. *Journal of Learning Disability Research* **51** (10) 750–765.

Tyrer P, Oliver-Africano PC, Ahmed Z, Bouras N, Cooray S, Deb S, Murphy D, Hare M, Meade M, Reece B, Kramo K, Bhaumik S, Harley D, Regan A, Thomas D, Rao B, North B, Eliahoo J, Karatela S, Soni A & Crawford M (2008) Risperidone, haloperidol, and placebo in the treatment of aggressive challenging behaviour in patients with learning disability: a randomised controlled trial. *Lancet* **371** 57–63.

Unwin G & Deb S (2008) Psychiatric and behavioural assessment scales for adults with learning disabilities. *Advances in Mental Health in Learning Disability* **2** (4) 37–45.

Unwin GL & Deb S (2010) The use of medication to manage problem behaviours in adults with a learning disability: a national guideline. *Advances in Mental Health in Learning Disabilities* **4** (3) 4–11.

Chapter 10

Supporting yourself and your team

John Rose and Mark Burns

This chapter initially looks at the evidence for the impact of challenging behaviour on the well-being of care staff working directly with people with behaviour that challenges. While the impact of challenging behaviour on staff is subtle and staff who work with people whose behaviour is challenging do not always report high levels of stress, we will argue that the case for developing effective programmes of support and spending time to design work environments that help staff to cope with challenging behaviour better is compelling.

The evidence for a link between challenging behaviour and stress

To most people it might seem obvious that working with people who have learning disabilities and challenging behaviour can be a stressful experience, which necessitates that staff require support. Direct care staff will often say that challenging behaviour is stressful (Hastings, 2002). Other research has suggested an association between the demands placed on staff by the challenging behaviour of the people they care for and more objective measures of stress including questionnaires on burnout and stress (for example, Hatton *et al,* 1995; Jenkins, Rose & Lovell, 1997; Rose, 1999). However, these associations are often surprisingly weak when compared to other factors that contribute to stress. Some studies have found no direct associations between stress and challenging behaviour (for example, Howard *et al,* 2009).

Some studies suggest that the characteristics of organisations – that is the way the environment people work in is designed – rather than the behaviour of the individuals they support, have a more important influence on staff stress and well-being than challenging behaviour itself (Hatton *et al,* 1999). Recent research has examined a variety of relationships that staff have with different aspects of the organisation, colleagues and residents (Thomas & Rose, 2010). The relationships represented by the organisation and colleagues had a stronger association with burnout in staff than with the residents they worked with.

At first sight these findings are confusing and can lead to the conclusion that challenging behaviour is a relatively minor factor in the development of stress in care staff. However, new research is emerging that suggests it is an important factor but it does not inevitably lead to stress. For example, a study by Howard *et al* (2009) did not find an association between stress and challenging behaviour. The study compared staff in the community who experienced very little challenging behaviour to those who worked in a medium secure unit who encountered it more frequently along with more intense levels of challenging behaviour. There was no difference in the average levels of burnout reported by the two groups, which could lead to the conclusion that challenging behaviour was not an important variable in determining the level of burnout in these groups. However, participants from the medium secure setting reported higher self-efficacy when compared to community participants and self-efficacy moderated the relationship between the challenging behaviour they experienced and burnout. That is, the staff in the secure unit felt more able and better equipped to cope with challenging behaviour than the community staff.

Evidence is also emerging that staff perceptions of challenging behaviour and the type of challenging behaviour experienced (Dilworth *et al*, in press; Phillips & Rose, 2010; Rose & Cleary, 2007) may also play an important role. This suggests that if appropriate support and training is provided to staff by the organisation to cope with challenging behaviour, these measures will reduce the impact of challenging behaviour on staff well-being.

Assessing the situation – measuring support

Organisations are complex and those that serve people with learning disabilities are no exception to this rule. The personalisation agenda, driven by recent social policy (DH, 2009), the huge diversity of people who work in services, and the great variety of individuals they support mean that services are variable in their design and can have very different characteristics. As a result, a large number of factors can contribute to stress in care staff (for example Rose, 2009). It might be evident to managers and workers that there are difficulties in an organisation and that some basic changes can be introduced easily. However, it might be hard to determine exactly what those problems are and how to resolve them without a more detailed assessment. Questionnaires exist that can help with the assessment of staff support in services (for example Rose *et al,* 2010; Rose, 1999). These can be used to collect data from groups of staff on the difficulties they face and their perceptions of the help they are currently receiving to meet these demands. While the use of such a questionnaire is recommended, sufficient resources need to be allocated to the job.

So that people feel they can share their true feelings it is best if they can be assured of anonymity. Questionnaires need to be completed anonymously and sent for analysis by someone who is not directly working in the organisation. The results can then be summarised and fed back to the group as general findings (not relating to any one individual) and discussed in general terms with the staff. Discussion in the staff group can lead to an action plan and the development of a series of goals that require specific changes to be completed by designated members of staff including managers (Rose *et al,* 2005). If support to analyse the questionnaires is not available, they can be used to guide a discussion between members of a staff team, however, it might be difficult for everyone to be open and honest, especially if the problems are perceived to be severe.

An organisational support framework

There is a large range of strategies that can help increase staff support. It is unlikely that they are all going to be appropriate and necessary in each organisation. However, it is useful to have an overview of the elements of a good support package so that a team can consider which strategies need development. A possible framework for staff support is provided by Rose *et al* (2010) and is shown in Table 10.1.

Table 10.1: An organisational support framework

Proactive	Reactive	Responsive
■ Person-centred values and skills ■ Acknowledgement of communicative aspects of challenging behaviour ■ Risk assessment/risk-management culture ■ Reflective practice groups ■ Supervision ■ Stress-management processes	■ Appropriate physical skills training ■ Post-incident support	■ Incident analysis ■ Individual support (formal and informal) ■ Psychological support

One feature of this framework is that it highlights the significance of support structures that are embedded within an organisation. If organisational processes are designed to support staff then it is unlikely that staff will experience excessive levels of stress. Systems can be designed to prevent stressors from directly impacting on staff and help staff to cope in a responsive way to any event, such as challenging behaviour, that occurs. Many of the processes highlighted in Table 10.1 are proactive and can help build a supportive team that will help the team members become resilient to stressors when they occur. Other support strategies can be built into policies and procedures so that the organisation can respond reactively to immediate challenges whereas others can be put in place over a longer period of time to try and develop more robust plans and systems.

Proactive strategies

The organisational support framework highlights the importance of person-centred values and skills (DH, 2009). It is vital that a staff team has a common philosophy and plans so that the team can work together to meet its aims, if the group does not share the same values then there is always likely to be tension within it. It is not sufficient to expect care staff to acquire this knowledge without specific training and organisations need to have written information available that is provided in an appropriate form and implemented by more senior staff. It is important to provide services and support to people with a learning disability based on an understanding of individual preferences, requirements and important routines. Phillips and Rose (2010) suggest that the way that staff interpret the challenging behaviour of residents is likely to influence decisions on whether they are asked to leave their homes as a result of challenging behaviour. The provision of person-centred services and support increases the likelihood of service users having personally satisfying lifestyles and power-balanced relationships with those providing the support. These factors should decrease the likelihood of challenging behaviour occurring.

Information also needs to be made available to staff about the nature of challenging behaviour and how to understand it more effectively. This can be done in a variety of ways; through short courses or by inviting external advisors in to help staff to understand the possible reasons for an individual's challenging behaviour. Challenging behaviour is often an individual's communication about their dissatisfaction with their physical or social environment, or the nature of the support being provided (Emerson, 2001). If the communication can be understood more fully it may be possible to reduce the challenging behaviour or, if not, achieving a greater understanding of the communicative function of the challenging behaviour may at least enable staff to take a more sympathetic attitude towards the individual concerned. It has been found that where staff are less blaming towards residents, they are more likely to offer more effective support (Dilworth *et al,* in press).

Risk assessment and developing an effective risk-management culture is an important element in supporting staff to cope with challenging behaviour. A robust risk-management culture may have accounted for the similar levels of burnout found in Howard *et al*'s paper (2009) where staff in a medium secure unit reported similar levels of burnout to staff in community facilities. If an individual behaves in ways that challenge others there needs to be an assessment of the various environmental, social and personal factors associated with the occurrence of the behaviour. A robust plan needs to be developed to manage or ameliorate identified risks, and this needs to be reviewed regularly and updated in the light of new information. This ensures that risks to people using services or staff through occurrences of challenging behaviour are minimised and managed as far as is possible. It is also likely that staff are less likely to be fearful of assault and are more able to cope with any challenging behaviour that does occur if this is done (Rose & Cleary, 2007; Rose & Howard, 2010).

Reflective practice groups and supervision both provide a systematic way to consider events in a supportive environment focused on professional development. They should facilitate a discussion of challenges and personal impacts associated with supporting individuals whose behaviour can challenge and help to examine, clarify and validate individual or team practice. They allow reflection on the impact of work on individuals, and how this in turn affects professional practice. They can also create opportunities for positive feedback and the identification of, and planning the meeting of, support needs.

Stress-management processes and workshops can also be built into daily work schedules, for example mindfulness techniques (a form of meditation) have been shown to have beneficial effects for both staff and people using services (Singh *et al,* 2006).

Reactive strategies

There are a number of things that can be done immediately after an incident occurrs. Appropriate physical skills training can be an important element in a support package as training in the use of safe, ethical, socially valid and legal means of breakaway and use of brief physical restraint can provide staff with the knowledge and skills to maintain the safety of themselves and people using services (Hawkins *et al,* 2005). Again, this can reduce the fear of assault (Rose & Cleary, 2007) and give staff a safer structure to work in. However, care will need to be taken to ensure physical intervention skills are regularly updated and that they are embedded in policy and practice as a last resort to maintain safety. Systems also need to be in place to provide short, medium and long-term support to staff following a behavioural incident. This needs to be done to ensure that staff are well supported, to reduce stress levels, and identify remedial actions and provide opportunities for staff to learn from incidents.

Responsive strategies

Responsive strategies can also be put into place after an incident but will take longer to implement than reactive strategies. Incident analysis involves examining each occurrence of challenging behaviour with a view to identifying environmental and personal factors that appear to be associated with the occurrence of the behaviour. This can help with understanding the possible communicative function of challenging behaviour and assessing the influence of staff responses on challenging behaviour. This process can contribute to the risk assessment and management process. It can also lead to the identification of key triggers and enable preventative steps to be initiated.

After an incident of challenging behaviour, a staff member will require support. There are differing types of support – practical, emotional, psychological – and they can be delivered formally or informally. Support may need to be delivered over a variety of different time frames from short to long term. The main aim of this will be to reduce stress and burnout, but also to ensure that staff members feel valued and supported. It will also ensure that lessons can be learnt in relation to individuals whose behaviour is described as challenging.

The provision of more formalised psychological support may be useful when an individual is struggling after incidents of challenging behaviour. This may relate to fear, loss of confidence or doubting own abilities, and should be provided by someone with counselling or therapy skills. It provides a safe and confidential context to look at emotional issues that arise in relation to challenging behaviour and the impact on personal well-being and work performance.

The emerging evidence is becoming much clearer: challenging behaviour can be very stressful, however it does not need to be and there are a wide range of strategies that can be adopted to help cope with its impact. The best organisations and employers will have a range of provisions in place to support staff and with the right systems in place challenging behaviour can be managed effectively. While reducing challenging behaviour can be an important goal, having a staff support strategy will enable maintenance to be viewed as a viable option that can provide a reasonable quality of life for many individuals. This agenda fits with recent guidance on *Enabling Capable Environments* (Hopkins & Clover, 2010) that not only emphasises support for people using services but for staff as well. With some thought it is possible for all organisations to implement appropriate and effective support strategies. This chapter provides some suggestions for a way forward.

Conclusion

- The link between challenging behaviour and stress is not always clear as there are many factors that can influence this association.
- A thorough assessment is important to identify stressors so that interventions can be designed to meet the needs of a staff group.
- There are a large range of strategies that can help increase staff support.
- Proactive strategies designed to prevent stress should be the primary concern of all organisations.

References

Department of Health (2009) *Valuing People Now: A new three-year strategy for people with learning disabilities.* London: TSO.

Dilworth J, Phillips N & Rose J (In press) Factors relating to staff attributions of control over challenging behaviour. *Journal of Applied Research in Learning Disabilities.*

Emerson E (2001) *Challenging Behaviour: Analysis and intervention in people with learning disabilities* (2nd edition). Cambridge: Cambridge University Press.

Hastings RP (2002) Do challenging behaviours affect staff psychological well-being? Issues of causality and mechanism. *American Journal on Mental Retardation* **6** 455–467.

Hatton C, Brown R, Caine A & Emerson E (1995) Stressors, coping strategies and stress-related outcomes among direct care staff in staffed houses for people with learning disabilities. *Mental Handicap Research* **8** 252–271.

Hatton C, Emerson E, Rivers H, Mason H, Mason L, Swarbrick R, Kiernan C, Reeves D & Alborz A (1999) Factors associated with staff stress and work satisfaction in services for people with learning disability. *Journal of Learning Disability Research* **43** 253–267.

Hawkins S. Allen D & Jenkins R (2005) The use of physical interventions with people with learning disabilities and challenging behaviour: the experiences of service users and staff members. *Journal of Applied Research in Learning Disabilities* **18** (1) 19–34.

Hopkins L & Clover W (2010) *Enabling Capable Environments. Challenging Behaviour – National Steering Group.* Available from: http://www.thecbf.org.uk/pdf/CapableEnvironments.pdf (accessed 27 June 2011).

Howard R, Rose, J & Levinson V (2009) The psychological impact of violence on staff working with adults with learning disabilities. *Journal of Applied Research in Learning Disabilities* **22** (6) 538–548.

Jenkins R, Rose J & Lovell C (1997) Psychological well-being of staff working with people who have challenging behaviour. *Journal of Learning Disability Research* **41** 502–511.

Phillips N & Rose J (2010) Predicting placement breakdown: individual and environmental factors associated with the success or failure of community residential placements for adults with learning disabilities. *Journal of Applied Research in Learning Disabilities* **23** (3) 201–213.

Rose J (1999) Demands, supports and residential staff: a factor analytic study. *Journal of Learning Disability Research* **43** 268–278.

Rose J, Rose D & Hodgkins C (2005) Staff stress and coping strategies. In: G Holt, S Hardy & N Bouras (Eds.) *Mental Health in Learning Disabilities: A reader.* Pavilion Publishing: Brighton.

Rose J & Cleary A (2007) Care staff perceptions of challenging behaviour and fear of assault. *Journal of Learning and Developmental Disabilities* **32** (2) 153–161.

Rose J (2009) Staff stress and people who have mental health needs living in new models of service. *Advances in Mental Health and Learning Disabilities* **3** (2) 20–25.

Rose J, Harris P & Burns M (2010) Supporting yourself and your team. In: S Hardy & T Joyce (Eds) *Challenging Behaviour: A training pack to develop good practice in working with people with learning disabilities whose behaviour is described as challenging.* Brighton: Pavilion Publishing.

Rose J & Howard R (2010) *Contemporary Issues in Learning Disabilities.* New York: Novapublishers.

Singh N, Lancioni G, Winton A, Curtis W, Wahler R, Sabaawi J, Singh J & McAleavey K (2006) Mindful staff increase learning and reduce aggression in adults with developmental disabilities. *Research in Developmental Disabilities* **27** (5) 545–558.

Thomas K & Rose JL (2010) The relationship between reciprocity and the emotional and behavioural responses of staff. *Journal of Applied Research in Learning Disabilities* **23** (2) 167–179.

Chapter 11

Autism and challenging behaviour

Peter Carpenter

A large proportion of adults with learning disabilities whose behaviour is described as challenging have autism. The reasons for this illustrate the common reasons for challenging behaviour; a failure to communicate, a failure to recognise the wishes of the person; a lack of recognition of what is disturbing the person; and a failure to provide an environment suitable for the person. It is a reasonable claim that people with autism test the capability of any service to provide support that is individually tailored and truly recognises a person as an individual. If a service can provide well for people with autism then it should be able to provide high-quality services for all. The high rate of challenging behaviour reflects the stress an environment produces on someone who has a less flexible range of coping strategies than others. Understanding the possible stressors and common coping strategies will help us reduce the challenges.

What is autism?

How we understand autism has changed over the years. In the past it was seen as a mental illness, namely 'childhood schizophrenia', and treated accordingly. After this, people with autism were diagnosed by having the so-called 'triad of impairments' of social interaction, social communication and social imagination, with prominent rituals or routines.

Autism is now recognised as a condition that is defined by a cluster of behaviours rather than any neurological test. Society is starting to see people with autism as individuals who, for a variety of reasons, have difficulty processing variable and complicated patterns of behaviour, such as social communication and interaction. This is because internal communication in their brain is different. Autism is now known as a neuro-developmental condition, and not an illness.

At the severe end of disability there are often strong similarities between individuals who have autism, however, you must never assume that you understand an individual's wishes and needs just because they have autism. How a person grows up depends on the interaction between their difficulties and their experiences and, just like anyone else, people with autism learn coping strategies throughout their lives. When you meet a person with autism you are meeting both their autistic processing difficulties and how they have learnt to cope with the world. As a result, you must never forget the person with autism who, for example, may be feeling lonely or be dismissive of others (or both). A one-size-fits-all approach does not work with people with autism, just as it would not work with any other group.

Having autism does not mean you are mentally ill and it does not make you respond to events in a psychotic or illogical manner. Many of the coping strategies that make people with autism stand out are 'normal' strategies that have continued as they have developed, when others have learnt to suppress them. For example, you may be anxious and desperate to shut out stress and use methods like rocking, flapping or repeating words to calm down. When a baby or child does this it is seen as a 'normal' coping strategy, but when you are older and still do it, it is seen as 'autistic'.

For someone with autism, their whole life experience of developing is affected and modified by the filter imposed by the cause of their autism. Many of the stages seen as vital for 'normal' development can be altered. For example, attachments to parents may not be of the same nature; seeing the world as secure and not frightening may well never happen; developing a sense of oneself through interacting with others is altered; and learning to behave in a socially acceptable manner – such as not talking aloud to oneself – may be more difficult. As we grow up and interact with others we learn to regulate ourselves – to hold back on what we say and to suppress our feelings in certain situations. Many able people with autism may appear to be more socially 'immature' as they have not learnt the rules as quickly as others.

Sensory issues in people with autism

One of the common issues with people with autism is that they often have anomalies in how they feel things through their senses (Leekam *et al*, 2007). There are estimates that this occurs in over 90% of people with autism. There is evidence that suggests there is an anomaly in experiencing certain sensations. There is also the issue of how a person learns to deal with a sensation and communicates it to others. So, for example, there is not just evidence that a person may be insensitive to pain, but a lot of experience that they may not recognise what pain is or what is a useful way to respond when in pain, for example, to tell others.

We have many types of sensory receptors on our bodies. These include the five senses of sight, hearing, smell, taste and touch, as well as:

- fine touch
- deep pressure
- vibration
- balance
- proprioception (joint position sense)
- temperature
- pain
- internal organ stretch sensors (in gut, bladder, lungs etc).

We have a lot more sensory receptors than those in the above list. For example, our sight relies on the three sensations of red–green, blue–yellow and light–dark, and our sense of taste includes separate senses for salt, sweet, bitter, sour and umami (ie. savory).

There is a lot of evidence to show that people with autism have sensory problems. This would be expected if there are processing and communication difficulties within the brain – one would expect it to include difficulties in more basic issues such as integrating sensory experiences as well as processing related to social interaction.

The way that a person with autism has difficulty processing a sensation is highly varied. They can be oversensitive, or under sensitive, to the entire sense, or can have problems with just a certain part of the sensation (for example, just one pitch of sound). They can have difficulty modulating it – filtering out irrelevancies such as background conversation, or the ticking of a clock. The result of these sensory anomalies is often dramatically abnormal behaviour that calls attention to the person or makes them look unpredictable and 'psychotic'. For example, a person sitting in the corner with their fingers in their ears, or someone who strokes the hair of everyone they meet.

Sensory difficulties may cause people to display odd behaviours. Examples can include:

- a person who does not like showers because they dislike the sensation of water hitting their skin
- a person who does not like the high-pitched echoing sounds in the bathroom
- a person who suddenly becomes distressed several minutes before you hear a plane or car passing by
- a person who only eats pasta and mashed potatoes as they dislike spicy food
- a person who freezes when they come to steps or slopes because their joint position sense is poor and they do not have the confidence to know where their feet are as they move down a slope or kerb
- a person who sniffs people or who won't enter rooms because of a smell in the room/the flicker of fluorescent lights/the hum of electrics
- a person who strips off their clothes because they irritate their skin too much, or has to wear them ridiculously tight to move the sensation from one of touch, which is painful, to one of pressure, which is easier to manage.

Sensations may also be very enjoyable and more pleasurable than social interaction. As a result, the person may become absorbed, for example, in stroking things.

Communication

One of the issues discussed in other chapters is the importance of communication. In people with autism, communication is extremely significant as individuals tend to have characteristic communication patterns that are easily misinterpreted and can cause the person to become frustrated and display challenging behaviour.

First, there is the concentration on the literal meaning of words. A person with autism will concentrate on exactly what is said and will not modify what is said according to the context, the speaker's non verbal communication, or their intonation. Second, is the ability to use words without knowing their full meaning. This comes of hearing the words but not processing them at more abstract levels. This is most obvious when a person repeats words they have just said. A person who has learned more about how to talk may use phrases they have heard almost like a tape recorder, and reuse them in situations where they have heard them before. This makes the person look very capable. Another example is a person using 'you' to mean 'I' and 'I' to mean 'you' as this was how they heard them said. For example, when someone said 'you must get a drink' to the person, they realised that 'you' means them, but they have not realised that this is a relative pronoun, describing the relationship to the speaker, and not the listener.

If there is not a problem with knowing the meaning of the words, then another common problem is that the person with autism cannot process what is being said at the speed at which it is spoken. A person may understand the first few words in a conversation but as the speech goes on without break to give them time to 'catch up', they end up with a jumble of things to process. In this situation, an individual may seize on their personal key words and fill in what they want to hear. So they may think that you are saying the opposite to what you actually said. People with autism can have problems with working in the abstract and this can mean that being asked to make choices is 'difficult'.

People with autism respond best to those who:

- speak calmly and slowly, or in short sentences
- name them when talking ie. 'John, go and wash' not 'you need to wash'
- leave out superfluous words
- tell them in concrete terms what to do rather than what not to do
- talk in the here and now rather than the future
- check out their understanding when needed, without being too intrusive
- limit choices and present choices visually rather than in the abstract.

Distress

Another common source of challenging behaviour in people with autism is physical distress. Psychological distress is also common but carers tend to forget that people with autism get physically distressed – they experience pain or become hot, hungry or tired like anyone else. However, they may not realise to tell people and an onlooker will just see their 'disturbed behaviour'. If someone has a relatively sudden onset of challenging behaviour, you should question – 'are they in pain?' Common sources of pain are toothache, earache, but also cystitis and acid reflux.

Psychological distress can be another source of distress for a person with autism. Some may think that because many people with autism cannot describe their emotions then they cannot feel them. The opposite is usually the case. For example, a person with autism may understand that their mother has died or that their key worker has changed, and tell you why it happened and what is different as a result. They may even have learnt to label the emotion they are feeling as people tell them 'You are feeling sad'. However, they may not have processed the feeling. Most people process feelings by talking about them and describing them, and so ordering them in their minds. If you cannot process the meaning of the feelings and understand them, then the distress may continue for months or years after the event.

Emotional and mental health problems

Almost everyone with autism is more anxious than other people. This is because the world is a more confusing and unpredictable place, and it needs more work to survive in. However, many people with autism do not have the vocabulary or social awareness to describe feeling anxious. They may describe the physical signs accurately, but may worry people by describing symptoms differently, for example having snakes or sharks in their body because they have not learnt to call the feeling 'butterflies in the stomach', and they may get referred to a psychiatrist.

Some people with autism cope with the anxiety by retreating into a 'nest' where they feel safe and secure, and may fight attempts to get them into the 'harsh' world outside. Some individuals may come out into the world but rely on others to show them what to do. Others may make the world more predictable by whatever means they can – such as imposing a routine on themselves and those around them, or by regulating interaction with others by upsetting them (it is easier to upset someone than to please them). More able people with autism who are keen to interact with others often describe a social anxiety when they develop a classic social performance anxiety and behave accordingly.

What many describe though is 'fragmentation' – their anxiety overload in the environment is so overwhelming that their mind breaks down and mentally fragments. The person may then present as being psychotic. This sounds terrifying and those who have experienced it say you become desperate to avoid it. You become desperate to be alone, to retreat and can have a severe outburst to get everyone out of your way. Others may see it as a 'tantrum' or 'challenging behaviour', but this is an internal scream that can make the person avoid a situation.

As one might expect with a person who is anxious and uses rituals and routines to calm themself down, people with autism can develop obsessive compulsive disorder. If they do not do a certain act or repetitive thought, then they get more anxious. However, people often confuse matters by saying that a person has an 'obsession' about something when they mean a 'preoccupation'. For example, when they are doing something repeatedly because they want to and are enjoying doing it. Most people with autism have preoccupations, but some also have an obsession or compulsion.

Generalised anxiety, secondary to one's experience of the world, is very difficult to treat as the world is so confusing. It responds as well (if not better) to making the world more predictable with a safe area, clear routines and structured support, as much as to medication (which may well have to go to 'heroic' levels to work).

In addition, many people with autism have mood disorders. At the simplest level this may be an unstable mood, much like a child who has not yet learnt (or had the neurological maturity) to have a stable mood – the person's mood depends on the last thing they did or last person they spoke to. They can also develop a serious depression or mania (see Chapter 16). Again, it can be difficult to get the person to describe the feeling and we may only pick up that the person is depressed as they become more irritable and want to be left alone. However, careful observation will often show that the person shows all the hallmarks of depression – poor appetite, poor sleep, loss of enjoyment and loss of interests.

More able people with autism can find that one way to cope with anxiety is to drink alcohol or take drugs, and become addicted to them. One problem here is that the conventional treatment of 'alcoholism' is to let the person reach a choice about their drinking. Most people with autism find making that choice in the abstract very difficult and need to be given a much more concrete path to follow with targets. People with autism may have other disorders and neurological conditions such as attention deficit hyperactivity disorder (ADHD), epilepsy, eating disorders and Tourette's syndrome, and may also develop physical health problems like any other person.

Principles of managing challenging behaviour in people with autism

- Try to work out why the behaviour is occurring.
  - Is it a sensory processing issue?
  - Is it pain or physical disorder?
  - Is it the way we are communicating or the level we are operating at?
  - Are they being overloaded with choices etc?
  - Is it additional mental distress or illness?
  - What dangers or risks are there that we have to deal with?
- Then make the plan.
  - How do we change the environment to reduce stress?
  - What helps to calm them?
  - What do they enjoy doing?
  - What skills are needed (in carers and in person)?
  - What are we trying to achieve?

Conclusion

- People with autism are highly varied in their needs and reactions to others.
- People with autism have a developmental disorder and not an illness.
- Sensory anomalies are common and can make the person highly challenging if not understood.

- Recognising the difficulties in communicating is key to minimising any behavioural issues.
- Additional problems are common.

References

Leekam SR, Nieto C, Libby SJ, Wing L & Gould J (2007) Describing the sensory abnormalities of children and adults with autism. *Journal Autism Developmental Disorders* **37** (5) 894–910.

Further reading

See also information sheets issued by National Autistic Society on their website www.nas.org.uk - for example 'Mental Health and Asperger Syndrome'

Chapter 12

Challenging behaviour – who challenges who?

Peter Cronin

What does challenging behaviour mean?

Challenging behaviour means different things to different people. For example, what you think is challenging I might think is normal. Challenging behaviour can be someone shouting or someone being aggressive. But, you have to remember there is a reason for challenging behaviour. You need to think about how people have been treated in the past as this might cause challenging behaviour.

Why do you think challenging behaviour happens?

There are lots of reasons. A lot of the time it's because people have nothing to do – they're bored. Also, it can be a communication problem, especially with people with severe learning disabilities as they can't get their point of view across. They might not understand what staff are saying and they might get angry. They might not be able to tell staff what they want, even something simple like wanting a drink. Sometimes people get angry because of the staff. Staff can be challenging as well. They might tell you off or be too bossy. Staff need to have the right attitude and remember that they can get it wrong sometimes.

Do you have any examples of how staff behaviour can be challenging?

One time I came downstairs in the morning in my dressing gown and there was a stranger in the kitchen. I was shocked and frightened. It turned out she was a member of agency staff but no one had told us she was coming. That was challenging.

Sometimes the staff change the TV channel without asking and then wonder why I get upset. It's my house, not theirs. We have a house diary and sometimes they forget to write my appointments in and I miss important meetings. But, most of the time, they are kind and helpful – I don't want you to get the wrong idea!

What can help?

Staff need to be patient. They need to find out ways to communicate with people with learning disabilities. They need to find out what people want and help them get it. It's about respect as well; we need to be respected and people need to know that we have the same rights as everyone else. There's too much discrimination against people with learning disabilities.

People need things to do and not just sit in front of the TV all day. If someone can do a job then staff need to help them to find a job. Other people might want to go to a day centre or to classes. If you have things to do then you won't have challenging behaviour.

What should staff do when challenging behaviour happens?

They shouldn't panic. They should be calm and make sure everyone is safe. They could talk to the person gently and try and find out what's wrong. You could do relaxation exercises like taking deep breaths or going for a walk so they can calm down. Staff shouldn't be in the person's face – you need to give people space.

Chapter 13

Legal aspects

Ian Hall, Amanda Sinai, Theresa Joyce and Steve Hardy

Important legal considerations

Supporting people with learning disabilities and challenging behaviour requires an understanding of the relevant legal aspects. The law works to protect the person with learning disabilities as well as the people and organisations that support them. The European Court of Human Rights specifies that no one should be deprived of their liberty, unless it is in accordance with a procedure prescribed by law. There are specific laws for circumstances when it may be necessary to deprive someone of their liberty (OPG, 2008).

The Mental Capacity Act (England and Wales) (2005) (DCA, 2005) provides a clear framework for how to assess whether a person has capacity for a specific decision. If a person has capacity to make decisions about how they behave then they are responsible for their behaviour. If a person lacks capacity to make decisions about their behaviour in particular circumstances then they should be supported using the Mental Capacity Act. Principles include making a decision in the person's best interests and using the least restrictive intervention. The Mental Health Act (England and Wales) (2007) (DH, 2007) can be used to assess and/or manage a person with a mental disorder, when there are concerns that they may pose a risk to their health or safety, or the safety of others.

It is important to consider what parts of the law can allow a person to physically intervene to protect a person whose behaviour is challenging. Where a person is under the care of an organisation or authority, that organisation may be negligent if they do not provide adequate support for the person. It is therefore important that care providers have appropriate systems in place to support people whose behaviour is described as challenging.

The Sexual Offences Act (2003) can be used in cases where the challenging behaviour is related to sexual offences (HM Government, 2003).

Case study: Mary

Mary is a twenty-three-year-old woman with learning disabilities. She lives with her family and attends a day centre during the week. She has support workers who help her get ready for the day centre and also support her in the evenings and on weekends.

Recently Mary has started to hit her face. Staff have also noticed that when they support Mary to clean her teeth, her gums bleed; she is also refusing to take part in some of her normal activities. The staff supported Mary to visit her dentist but she refused to open her mouth to be examined.

The staff team with the support of a psychologist developed a programme to desensitise Mary to the dental procedure, but it was unsuccessful.

The dentist would like Mary to have a general anaesthetic so that a thorough assessment of her teeth can be completed and any treatment that is required can be initiated.

Case study: Abdul

Abdul is a thirty-two-year-old man with learning disabilities. He lives with his parents and his younger brother. He has support workers three times a week who take him shopping and to his gym class.

In the past month, Abdul's family and his support workers have noticed that he has been quieter and prefers to spend more time in his room. For the past two weeks he seems scared when he goes out of the house. He has started to shout at people on the street and says things like 'don't look at me' and 'stop following me'. He has also started hitting his ear and banging his head against the wall. On one occasion he gave himself a black eye. His brother is reluctant to take him to Friday prayers because of the changes in his behaviour. Abdul's family and support workers are worried about him.

Mental capacity

People make decisions every day of their lives. These can be small, insignificant decisions such as what to wear or eat, or more serious decisions that have significant consequences such as having medical treatment or moving home. The vast majority of people are able to make these decisions, but sometimes an individual may lack capacity to make specific decisions and the law has been developed (or is being developed throughout the UK) to address such instances. In England and Wales there is the Mental Capacity Act (DCA, 2005), in Scotland there is Adults with Incapacity (Scottish Executive, 2000) and Northern Ireland is currently developing its law on capacity.

Mental capacity law states that before an individual can be deemed as having or lacking capacity to make a particular decision, an assessment of capacity should be completed. The assessment would normally be completed by the individual that will implement the decision. For example, with decisions around surgery it would be the surgeon who is responsible for assessing capacity.

Prior to the assessment the individual being assessed needs to have the relevant information about the decision. This may include the possible advantages and disadvantages of making the decision and of any alternatives. People with learning disabilities are likely to need extra support to understand this information. This may include alternative methods of presenting the information (for example, pictures and symbols), specialist advice (for example, speech and language therapy) and more time to process the information.

The assessment of capacity will test if the individual is able to understand and remember the information relating the decision. It will also assess how they have reached their decision – an important factor will be the person demonstrating that they used and weighed the information as part of this process. For example, the individual who is recommended to have a surgical procedure weighed up the potential benefits to their health and lifestyle, while also contemplating the potential risks of the procedure. The assessor will ask the individual a range of questions to test these factors. If they do not know the individual well they may ask for others to support the process, such as learning disability specialists.

If the person is assessed as having capacity then it is their decision to make. If they are assessed as lacking capacity to make this particular decision then it can be made in their best interests. As with the capacity assessment, the person responsible for making the best interests decision is the person who will implement it, but they should consult with those engaged in caring for or working with the individual.

When making a best interests decision the decision maker should consider the possible advantages and disadvantages from medical, emotional and social welfare perspectives. Although the individual lacks capacity to make the decision, their past and present wishes, beliefs and values should still be considered. In some instances a 'best interests' meeting may be held. This would provide an opportunity for all those involved in the person's care to contribute to the decision-making process.

In England and Wales there are some decisions that are considered so personal that the Mental Capacity Act states that only a person with capacity can make them, and a best interests decision can never be made. These include sexual relationships, marriage, voting and adoption. There are some decisions that can only be made by the Court of Protection – a court that specially deals with issues of capacity. These decisions include organ and bone marrow donation and non-therapeutic sterilisation.

Case study: Mary

The dentist gave information to Mary's support workers about the procedure (including the anaesthetic) and the possible benefits and risks. The support staff spent several weeks giving this information to Mary, using accessible information on dental procedures specifically designed for people with learning disabilities.

After the two weeks Mary visited her dentist for an assessment of capacity. Mary was able to answer some of the questions, but had great difficulty in showing that she had used and weighed the information to come to a decision. The dentist thought that Mary lacked the capacity to make this decision. She decided that it was in Mary's best interests to have the procedure as it would improve her quality of life as the pain she was experiencing would be reduced; she would no longer hurt herself; and she could take part in the activities she liked. Mary has also had two general anaesthetics in the past with no ill effect.

The Mental Health Act

Challenging behaviour can be an indication that a person with a learning disability has a mental health problem such as depression, anxiety or psychosis. In this case, it may be appropriate to consider use of the Mental Health Act. It should be said that most mental health problems can be treated without using the Mental Health Act, but sometimes it is necessary to use when assessment or treatment in hospital is required, or in limited circumstances for treatment in the community.

The Mental Health Act (England and Wales) can be used to assess and/or manage a person with a mental disorder when there are concerns that this may pose a risk to their health or safety, or the safety of others. If a person with a learning disability does not have any other mental disorder apart from their learning disability, the Mental Health Act can only be used if there is associated abnormally aggressive or seriously irresponsible conduct.

A Mental Health Act assessment decides whether or not it would be appropriate to assess and/or manage a person under the Mental Health Act. In most circumstances, two doctors (one of whom is an approved psychiatrist) and one approved mental health professional (AMHP) are required to conduct the assessment. An AMHP can be from several professions, but must have undertaken specific training in the Mental Health Act. It is preferable for these people to have prior knowledge of the person they are assessing, and expertise in supporting people with learning disabilities, but in some cases this might not be possible.

Most commonly, the Mental Health Act is used to detain people in hospital when they do not agree to admission themselves. The most common orders used are section 2 (up to 28 days for assessment) and section 3 (up to six months for treatment).

Supervised community treatment provides a way to support people in the community. The main sanction – if the person does not comply with the conditions of the community treatment order – is that they can be recalled to hospital. People can only be considered for supervised community treatment if they have been detained in hospital under certain sections of the Mental Health Act.

Guardianship is a part of the Mental Health Act that allows the appointment of a guardian (often the local social services authority) to help and supervise people in the community. There is a power to require the person to reside in a particular place, allow access to people supporting them, and to attend for 'treatment' (although there is no power to make the person take or engage in the treatment).

In contrast to the Mental Capacity Act, the Mental Health Act applies both to people who have capacity and people who lack capacity. Another difference is that decisions do not necessarily have to be made in the person's best interests, if the safety of others is an important consideration.

All people who are detained in hospital, or are subject to guardianship or supervised community treatment under the Mental Health Act have the right to appeal and they also have a right to legal representation. They also have the right to an independent mental health advocate (IMHA). It may be that they would benefit from support in order to access these.

Case study: Abdul

Abdul's family spoke with his GP, who checked for physical problems that might explain the problem, including ear infection. His GP did not find any physical health problems and referred Abdul to the psychiatrist. The psychiatrist thought he might have a psychotic illness, and prescribed some antipsychotic medication. A week later his behaviour had deteriorated, and the family were concerned he would seriously harm himself. The GP and the psychiatrist visited with a social worker (AMHP) to conduct a Mental Health Act assessment. Abdul did not want to go into hospital, but it was thought to be necessary to manage his behaviour safely and assess the underlying mental health problems. Abdul was admitted to hospital under section 2.

Deprivation of Liberty Safeguards

For people who lack capacity and are in hospital or living in residential care homes, there may be times when it is in their best interests to deprive them of their liberty. In England and Wales, the Deprivation of Liberty Safeguards (DoLS) have been developed to provide a legal process through which individuals are assessed as to whether their liberty is being deprived and a due legal process to safeguard their rights and ensure appropriate review (OPG, 2008). DoLS follows the principles of the Mental Capacity Act (2005).

A person may be deprived of their liberty if:

- they have a mental disorder
- they are lacking capacity to consent to care in a hospital or care home
- it is in their best interests to protect them from harm and it is proportionate to the likelihood and seriousness of that harm
- care can only be provided by a deprivation of their liberty.

It is quite common for hospitals and care homes to place restrictions on an individual's liberty for their own safety, for example the person may not leave their home unescorted due to a lack of road awareness and safety, but there are regular scheduled visits into the community. But when does restriction become deprivation? It is likely this will be defined as cases go through the courts, however, the DoLS Code of Practice (OPG, 2008) offers some guidance as to what amounts to a deprivation:

- staff control the person's care and movements for significant periods of time
- staff control their assessments, treatment, contacts and residence
- a request by carer for discharge is refused
- the person is unable to maintain social contacts due to restrictions
- the person loses autonomy
- the person has no access to the community.

DoLS provide a framework for assessment by a range of individuals. The assessment will be completed by several professionals, including approved doctors under the Mental Health Act, approved mental health professionals under the Mental Health Act, and trained best interests assessors. The assessment will include:

- that the person is over the age of 18
- that the person has not made a decision in advance (ie. when they had capacity) that conflicts with the application
- the person's capacity regarding this decision
- whether they have a mental disorder as defined by the Mental Health Act

- whether they are already detained under the Mental Health Act or meet the criteria for detention
- whether it is in their best interests.

If the assessment supports the deprivation of liberty, an authorisation of up to 12 months may be granted and may have conditions attached, such as regular staff support to visit family or access community activities. A representative will be appointed who will represent the person and maintain contact and support. The hospital or care home has an obligation to explain the authorisation and their rights to the person, including the right to challenge via the Court of Protection, the right to regular review etc. A review can be carried out by the authorising body at any time and the hospital or care home can terminate the authorisation if they think it is no longer required.

It is important to consider legal issues when supporting people with learning disabilities whose behaviour is challenging. This includes thinking about issues such as physical intervention, negligence and use of the Mental Capacity Act or Mental Health Act. The Mental Capacity Act provides a legal framework to support people whose behaviour is challenging who do not have the capacity to understand their actions. The Mental Health Act can be used to assess and/or manage a person with a mental disorder when there are concerns that this may pose a risk to their health, safety or the safety of others.

Conclusion

- The Mental Capacity Act provides a legal framework to support people who lack capacity to make decisions about how they behave.
- Challenging behaviour might mean that a person with a learning disability has an underlying mental health problem.
- The Mental Health Act can be used to assess and treat a person who has a mental health problem where their behaviour puts their own health or safety at risk, or is a risk to the safety of other people.

References

Department of Constitutional Affairs (2005) The Mental Capacity Act. London: TSO.

Department of Health (2007) The Mental Health Act: Amended. London: TSO.

HM Government (2003) Sexual Offences Act. London: TSO.

Office of the Public Guardian (2008) Deprivation of Liberty Safeguards Code of Practice. London: TSO.

Scottish Executive (2000) Adults with Incapacity (Scotland) Act. Edinburgh: The Scottish Executive.

Chapter 14

Working in partnership with families

Viv Cooper

This chapter considers the role of family in the lives of people with learning disabilities whose behaviour is described as challenging. It will look at the diversity of family and family involvement, and explore what families have told us about their experiences. The current policy approach to families will be summarised, and there will be a discussion about how this can be put into practice, taking account of the need for flexibility to understand the family perspective. The benefits of partnership working will be discussed, with practical suggestions about working together with families to deliver better outcomes for individuals.

What is 'family'?

Most individuals have people in their lives that are described as 'family', although what constitutes a family varies greatly. Equally, the level of involvement of family in a person's life varies enormously and can change at different times. However, most of us value the love and support that our family provides and their involvement (at whatever level) in our lives, which is usually long term. Anyone can have a child with learning disabilities and so there is a wide diversity of family situations and types – there is no such thing as a 'typical' family.

Valuing People (DH, 2001a) acknowledges the importance of families in the lives of people with learning disabilities: *'Caring for a family member with a learning disability is a lifelong commitment, which continues even when the person is living away from the family home. Carers make a vital contribution to the lives of people with learning disabilities, often providing most of the support they need. They are a crucial resource for ensuring that people with learning disabilities can live in the community. Statutory agencies do not always properly recognise the extent of carers' contribution or its value.'*

People with learning disabilities whose behaviour is challenging to services are likely to be marginalised and disadvantaged – therefore it is even more important that beneficial family relationships are maintained and encouraged. In addition, adults with learning disabilities and behaviour described as challenging are likely to be supported by a range of paid workers who may be very important to the individual but often only for a relatively short period in their lives. The continuity of family can therefore be particularly important.

What do we know about families of people with learning disabilities?

Families of disabled people have identified many positive aspects of caring. However, research has highlighted a range of ways in which families can be disadvantaged (Beresford, 1995). These include high levels of stress, financial disadvantage, adverse impact on the carers' health, feelings of isolation, poor housing and an increased rate of marital breakdown. The situation for some black and minority ethnic communities is qualitatively worse on a number of key indicators, including a high level of unmet needs, lack of information, poverty, poor housing, social isolation and lack of support.

Families of individuals with learning disabilities whose behaviour is described as challenging are likely to be more at risk of these disadvantages. We also know that people with learning disabilities who access services are supported by a range of people who come and go from their lives. Family members can often be the single 'constant' in a person's life.

'I will always be a part of my son's life – I know I am important to him even though he can't tell me that in words. I know that come what may, I can rely on my family to always be there for me – and it's even more important for him to have that too.' Parent

For people with complex needs, it is really important that their history, memories and past experiences are recalled and captured, and families can therefore be an important source of information not only for the person, but also for those who are providing their support.

Policy and best practice

There have been a range of policies in the last 10 years or so that have identified the importance of working in partnership with families. *Family Matters* (DH, 2001b) was published alongside *Valuing People* (DH, 2001a) and highlighted the three key themes that family carers said were important to them in order of priority:

- they wanted their role in supporting their family member with a learning disability to be recognised and valued
- they wanted to be treated as equal partners in planning the support of their family member
- they wanted some support in their own right as a carer.

It is important to note that, consistently, family carers focus not on themselves or their own support needs as carers but on getting the right care and support for their family member. Their key message is '*Get it right for them and you get it right for us.*'

The Carers Strategy (DH, 2008) – *Carers at the Heart of 21st Century: Families and communities* – re-stated a commitment to value the role of family carers, and when this strategy was refreshed (DH, 2010) it stated very clearly that '*carers will be respected as expert care partners...*'.

The Mansell Reports (DH, 1993; 2007 (revised)) set out what needs to be in place to support individuals with learning disabilities whose behaviour is described as challenging and the revised edition acknowledges that '*although there has been good progress ... since ... Valuing People, progress in respect of challenging behaviour has lagged behind.*'

The commitment of the government to personalisation is an opportunity for individuals whose behaviour is described as challenging – a move away from trying to 'fit people in' to existing services towards more individualised, person-centred support is entirely consistent with what research tells us works for people with complex needs. This holistic person-centred approach to support and services was identified within guidelines developed for clinicians and service providers in 2007. The unified approach (Royal College of Psychiatrists *et al,* 2007) advocates a multidisciplinary and multi-agency approach to improving the quality of people's lives.

The route to support and services: a family perspective

Although the policy aims are consistent – a person-centred, holistic and partnership approach to appropriate individualised support and services – the experience of how this translates into practice is variable. It is important for service providers to understand family experiences of support and services (or lack of them), and that these experiences may not have been positive.

Just as there is no 'typical' family of a person with learning disabilities whose behaviour is described as challenging, there is equally no set pathway to support and services. However, due to the complexity of the support needs of the individual there are some common features that most families of people with severe learning disabilities and behaviour described as challenging commonly report.

Information

Most families report a lack of clear, useful information – about the particular needs of their relative, or about the services and support available to meet those needs. The complexity of health, social care and education systems, compounded by a split in each of these for support and services available to children and adults can be confusing and unhelpful.

'It was difficult enough trying to come to terms with and manage my son's disability and behaviour – but understanding who does what, and how to get different bits of support from different people and different departments was a nightmare.' Parent

Support

Families consistently report that they do not get the appropriate support when or where they need it, and that there is a crisis management approach.

'I don't care whether support is funded from health or social care, or if there has been a recent re-organisation or change of priorities – I just want people who can provide me and my family with the help we need!' Parent

Partnership

Families want to be included as valued partners in the lives of their relatives.

'People with learning disabilities are often not supported in the most appropriate manner in my opinion, and parents can be seen as interfering, rather than as a partnership.' Parent

A recent review of support and services for individuals whose behaviour is described as challenging included interviews with families about their experiences of support and services (McGill *et al,* 2010).

Families reported:

- a lack of expertise and capability in understanding and responding to challenging behaviour in local services (which was seen as an important factor in use of out-of-area placements)
- great difficulty accessing services other than at times of crisis; as a result opportunities for crisis prevention were missed
- a lack of support and training for themselves in their roles as carers, with often detrimental effects on their own physical and mental health
- a lack of information and training that hampered the extent to which families could plan realistically, and hopefully, for the future
- not being included as essential partners in planning for their relatives.

The concerns of families contacting the Challenging Behaviour Foundation can broadly be defined as follows:

- the current service provision not meeting the needs of their relative (including lack of local service development and lack of individualised approaches)
- lack of information, training and practical support
- concerns about restrictive practices (including inappropriate use of seclusion, physical restraint and antipsychotic medication).

Given these experiences and circumstances, families may understandably be wary of support and service providers. Promoting a partnership approach with families can therefore be a skilful task requiring understanding and effort to develop a relationship of mutual trust, but the positive benefits that result are worth it.

Working together – delivering positive outcomes

A key point to remember is that most families want to work as partners. They want to be a positive influence in the life of their relative. Ultimately, families and service providers have the same fundamental aim; to enable the person to have a good quality of life that is rewarding and fulfilling.

Families have identified the following characteristics of good working relationships with support and providers:

- honesty
- respect for their opinions and perspectives
- respect for their expertise and experience.

'I want support providers to ask themselves: "Would you like to live your life like this? Would this be good enough for you? For your son, daughter or relative?" If the answer is no, then you need to change what you are you are doing.' Parent

An honest approach is essential to building trust. Sometimes there will be situations that cannot be changed for a variety of reasons, or situations beyond the control of the service provider – being honest about this helps everyone to understand what it is possible to change and what it is not, and to discuss this openly.

'From the outset, I said I wanted to be kept informed – if she is ill, if her behaviour deteriorates, if she doesn't get on with people, if something happens. I may be able to help, to shed some light on things. And we can put our heads together to find solutions.' Parent

The opinions, perspectives, expertise and experience of families should never be underestimated. It is important to remember that their role is long term – they are likely to hold far more information in their memories and experiences than can ever be captured in a file.

'I have met many families of people with learning disabilities in all sorts of situations. Sometimes family carers are described as "difficult" – but I have yet to meet a single one who is "difficult" for the sake of it. If a family carer is

"difficult" there is a reason – it may have been something that has happened recently, or many years ago – but there is a reason, usually a very good one, why they are distrustful, and they need support and understanding to build a new relationship…' Parent

Family carer support worker

In research conducted by Grant and Whittell (1999), families identified the following as things they valued and found helpful from services:

- a proactive approach
- flexibility
- consistency
- accessibility
- availability
- reliability.

Recent work of the Challenging Behaviour Foundation with Families (for the Department for Children Schools and Families) identified some 'top tips' for working with families as partners, which reflected the above principles. They wanted services/supporters to:

- find out the family's hopes and aspirations for the individual
- get off to a good start by making and maintaining early contact and agreeing how this will be done
- be clear, accurate, open and truthful
- keep language clear and simple so it cannot be misinterpreted – avoid jargon
- take the family's concerns seriously
- be an active and empathetic listener
- stay approachable and be contactable, even if you disagree
- personalise written communication and never use generic statements about an individual

- use creativity to seek out the individual's views, when appropriate
- signpost families to sources of independent advice and support.

Working in partnership should be a core principle on which all support and services for individuals with learning disabilities and behaviour described as challenging are based. Many families will have had difficult experiences of supporting their family member to access good quality, individualised support and services and the impact of this should be acknowledged. Families are a valuable resource, providing long-term support, experience and information that is unique. They can be powerful advocates and allies in supporting individuals whose behaviour is described as challenging, and investing in developing a good relationship with them will result in better outcomes for all.

Conclusion

- It is good practice to engage with family carers as partners – they can be powerful advocates and they bring a unique and long-term perspective.
- Most people value their relationship with their family, and most families want to be involved; invest in developing a good relationship.
- Families are diverse; there is no such thing as a typical family and they may have mixed experiences of support and services.
- Families value an honest approach that respects and values their experience and perspective.

References

Beresford B (1995) *Expert Opinions: A national survey of parents caring for a severely disabled child.* Bristol: The Policy Press.

Department of Health (1993) *Services for People with Learning Disabilities and Challenging Behaviour or Mental Health Needs (The Mansell Report).* London: TSO.

Department of Health (2001a) *Valuing People: A new strategy for learning disability for the 21st century.* London: TSO.

Department of Health (2001b) *Family Matters: Counting Families In.* London: TSO.

Department of Health (2007) *Services for People with Learning Disability and Challenging Behaviour or Mental Health Needs (revised edition).* London: TSO.

Department of Health (2008) *Carers at the Heart of 21st Century Families and Communities.* London: TSO.

Department of Health (2010) *Recognised, Valued and Supported: Next steps for the carers strategy.* London: TSO.

Grant G & Whittell B (1999) *Family Care of People with Learning Disabilities: Support for family coping.* Cardiff: University of Wales.

McGill P, Cooper V & Honeyman G (2010) *Developing Better Commissioning for Individuals with Behaviour that Challenges Services: A scoping review.* Canterbury and Chatham: The Tizard Centre and The Challenging Behaviour Foundation.

Royal College of Psychiatrists, British Psychological Association & Royal College of Speech and Language Therapists (2007) *Challenging Behaviour: A unified approach.* London: RCPsych.

Chapter 15

Active support

John Shephard and Peter Baker

High quality, well organised services for people with severe learning disabilities and challenging behaviour do not appear to develop naturally, or by accident; rather, it seems that if we want this to happen, we have to make it happen. Achieving such service quality should result in a number of positive outcomes for those who are served, including, for example, reduced levels of challenging behaviour, improved social networks, an enhanced image in the eyes of other people, and so on. Some of these outcomes could be seen, in a sense, as being indirectly accomplished – by-products of general lifestyle enhancements created by improved service design. But one of the more direct outcomes will be concerned with how people spend their time – their patterns of activity.

How we spend our time is a significant factor in determining the quality of our lives. Most of us are busy, with a wide range of things to attend to, deadlines to meet, family lives, homes and relationships to be maintained, amounting to a richness and variety that, as a rule, we value. A busy lifestyle can enhance our self-esteem, provide a sense of achievement when we attain our goals, and demonstrate that we are ourselves needed and valued. For many of us, for a variety of reasons, having paid employment is an important factor, not least because it helps us to finance other activities in our lives. In addition, a busy life means that we are able to appreciate times when we can rest, enjoy recreation or perhaps, for short periods, choose to do nothing.

Patterns of activity for people with severe learning disabilities, especially those with challenging behaviour, are often quite different. Such differences typically include:

- instead of having too much to do, they often have too little to do
- instead of being subject to the demands of their current life circumstances, they are often 'protected' from these by staff or carers who deal with such things for them

- there may be a complete absence of certain sorts of activities for example, work, which normally occupies a great deal of our time.

(McGill & Toogood, 1994)

For those living in residential services, the above are likely, in part, to be a product of environments that are poorly organised and that, typically, might be characterised by inadequate levels of staffing, a dearth of meaningful activity, a lack of structure and/or an emphasis on control. The danger here – and, for many, the reality – is that their daily routines will comprise a significant amount of empty time (during which nothing is achieved, and time cannot be re-lived): waiting for the next activity, sitting (allegedly) watching television, exhibiting stereotypical behaviours, and experiencing artificially, and unnecessarily, prolonged periods of 'rest'. The active support model has emerged as one solution to this phenomenon, and is predicated on the belief that engagement – the real and meaningful participation in the activities of daily life – is fundamentally important in the attainment of a rich quality of life.

Active support provides an organisational framework comprising a variety of systems and structures designed to provide environments that promote participation, engagement and skills development. Such systems and structures work in combination to provide a range of activity – a curriculum – through which these objectives can be pursued. The model addresses the issue of abnormal patterns of activity outlined above by seeking to:

- develop a curriculum that is relatively full and includes a range of activities (work, leisure, personal maintenance etc) that are present in a non-disabled person's life
- emphasise the requirements of the environment in which the service is provided, for example if this is a house, then the curriculum should typically include housework
- allow the person (within the constraints of typicality and environmental requirements) to choose their own pattern of activities.

(McGill & Toogood, 1994)

Each person's curriculum – whether they have a disability or not – is likely to be different in terms of balance and emphasis, reflecting our particular circumstances, needs and preferences. There will also be common ground, since we all have some similar needs – to keep healthy, have relationships, enjoy our leisure time, and so on. In general terms, the non-disabled population is able to arrange their lives and routines to accommodate their various needs and to achieve their goals. Active support recognises that people with learning disabilities and challenging behaviour require carefully planned and targeted assistance so that their lives are similarly efficiently organised.

While the different tools of active support can be deployed in varying combinations for each person according to their need, there will be a number of key components, common to all, used as a foundation for the supporting framework.

Person-centred plans (PCP)

There are a variety of person-centred plan models to choose from, which include *Planning Alternative Tomorrows with Hope* (PATHs) and *Making Action Plans* (MAPS) by Falvey *et al* (1997) and *Essential Lifestyle Planning* by Sanderson & Smull (2005). Deciding which model is the most appropriate for a person will be determined by a range of factors, including how well staff know them, and whether the plan is going to focus on the day-to-day considerations, or on the longer term objectives. In any case, the plan will, among other things, identify a set of goals and aspirations for each person to strive towards in the next phase of their life.

Activity plans

Each person's pursuit of their goals will in part be undertaken through the vehicle of their activities. The manner of their undertaking – how they are ordered, the way in which one activity flows into the next, how they intersect with each other and so on – will be guided by another level of planning additional to, and emanating from, the overarching PCP. Typically, these will include a variety of timetables, schedules and action plans, which will combine in order to co-ordinate the disparate activity components into a coherent and logical whole. Such planning will identify the detail both *across* activities, and *within* them. For example, a person's activity plans might include:

- a weekly plan – which determines that they will have opportunities to develop their skills in using the washing machine every Monday

- a daily plan – which determines that this will occur after breakfast
- a teaching plan – which determines how the activity will be carried out (the teaching style, the nature of prompting etc).

In addition, opportunity plans (Jones *et al,* 1996) might be used to serve as a reminder to staff to offer this activity (and others) according to the agreed schedule.

Shift plans

Whereas activity plans are largely concerned with how the person with learning disabilities will spend their time (and the nature of staff support), shift plans determine how staff in residential services will spend their time in the course of providing that support. The significance of the shift plan is that it will itemise, in necessary and sufficient detail, what will happen at that interface where the service provider and the person using the service meet, and, as such, has a highly direct impact on how people live their lives. In essence, the shift plan describes who will be doing what, with whom, and when, for that seven or eight-hour period of a shift; faulty planning at this stage, therefore, will have very real consequences. A good quality shift plan will take into account both the needs of the service (for example, the weekly shop needs to be done), and the needs of the individual (Susan needs to do her laundry today), as well as the resources available (staff and time). It will also allow for people's individual routines (for example, we don't all need to have our meals at the same time), and personal preferences (Susan enjoys housework, and takes particular pride in keeping her room tidy, while Bill likes to be out in the community as much as possible).

It is not intended that the shift plan imposes a rigid structure from which the participants cannot deviate; rather, it should include a degree of flexibility so that unexpected events can be accommodated with minimum disruption. Participants can then depart from the original plan for as long as required, and return to it when circumstances allow.

Recording systems

As in any model of practice, the extent to which active support is implemented in a given service, and its effectiveness, should not be left to anecdotal accounts to describe. Adequate methods of objective recording need to be established that can verify that the systems and structures that are planned to be in place are, actually, in place, and are achieving what they set out to achieve.

Typically, the active support model engenders a range of noteworthy processes and outcomes that are amenable to record-keeping, some of which are given below, with examples cited:

- a record that activities have been offered as per the schedule, for example *Keeping Track* (Brown *et al*, 1987) and *Opportunity Plans* (Jones *et al*, 1996)
- a record of how specific activities are to be offered, for example *Action Plans* (Hobbs, 2008)
- a record that teaching plans have been implemented as per the schedule, for example *Teaching Plans* (Jones *et al*, 1996)
- a record of each person's community activity, for example *The Guernsey Community Participation and Leisure Assessment* (Baker, 2000)
- a record of levels of engagement and staff assistance (for example Jones *et al*, 2001)
- a record of levels of challenging behaviours.

The above list is not intended to be exhaustive; it simply denotes the range of evidence that can be accrued in order to ascertain the extent to which an individual's person-centred plan is truly being enacted, rather than existing only as a set of promises that remain in a filing cabinet and are never realised.

Monitoring and evaluation systems

Much of the evidence generated from the recording systems above lends itself to being measured – how many activities were offered? What percentage of engagement was achieved? How much have people learnt from their skills-teaching opportunities? These outcomes can, in turn, be compared to targets that have been set in order that quantifiable measures of success can be calculated.

In addition, the use of video – whereby, for example, members of staff are filmed carrying out active support plans with individuals – can enable reflective practice to occur, in which staff can view themselves, and each other, and refine their practice accordingly. This is a particularly effective medium for attending to the finer detail of staff/individual interaction – for example, identifying the most helpful type of prompts and the naturally occurring cues within an activity in order to best promote participation and learning. Use of a written checklist (for example, *Teaching Strategy Checklist* by Hobbs, 2008) can further assist in this objective.

The overall effectiveness of active support can be evaluated by the *Periodic Service Review* (PSR) (LaVigna *et al,* 1994) – a process in which standards of service performance are agreed and then systematically reviewed on a regular basis – usually monthly in the first instance – resulting in a percentage of success. A minimum target of 85% is generally considered to be indicative of good quality.

Active support, when effectively implemented, can be a powerful means of positively changing people's lives. It provides a framework within which increasingly skilled and individually tailored staff performance creates opportunities for people with learning disabilities and challenging behaviour to become true participants, rather than passive observers, in lives of evolving richness and variety. This chapter has presented only an overview; the active support module in the accompanying training package provides a more 'hands-on' experience of it in action.

Conclusion

- Active support is an organisational framework comprising a variety of systems and structures designed to more effectively enable people with learning disabilities and challenging behaviour to become true participants in their lives. It achieves this by:
  - orchestrating staff support in a cohesive and efficient manner, taking account of each person's learning and interactional style
  - co-ordinating a person's timetables and activity schedules into a logical whole, characterised by a sense of rhythm and flow
  - effective recording, monitoring and evaluating outcomes.

References

Baker PA (2000) Measurement of the community participation and use of leisure of service users with learning disabilities: the Guernsey Community Participation and Leisure Assessment (GCPLA). *Journal of Applied Research in Learning Disabilities* **13** (3) 169–186.

Brown H, Toogood S & Brown V (1987) *Bringing People Back Home.* South East Thames Regional Health Authority: Bexhill-on-Sea.

Falvey MA, Forest M, Pearpoint J & Rosenberg RL (1997) *All My Life's a Circle. Using the tools: Circles, MAPS & PATHS.* Inclusion Press: Toronto.

Hobbs D (2008) Teaching practices and attitudes that facilitate change. *In: Positive Approaches to Challenges of Behaviour and Learning seminar.* Crowborough: Life of Your Own.

Jones E, Perry J, Lowe K, Allen D, Toogood S & Felce D (1996) *Active Support: A handbook for planning daily activities and support arrangements for people with learning disabilities.* Cardiff: Welsh Centre for Learning Disabilities Applied Research Unit.

Jones E, Felce D, Lowe K, Bowley C, Pagler J, Gallagher B & Roper A (2001) Evaluation of the dissemination of active support training in staffed community residences. *American Journal on Mental Retardation* **106** (4) 344–358.

La Vigna GW, Willis TJ, Shaull JF, Abedi M & Sweitzer M (1994) *The Periodic Service Review: A total quality assurance system for human services and education.* Baltimore: Brookes.

McGill P & Toogood S (1994) Organising community placements. In: E Emerson, P McGill & J Mansell (Eds) *Severe Learning Disabilities and Challenging Behaviours: Designing high quality services.* London: Chapman & Hall.

Sanderson H & Smull M (2005) *Essential Lifestyle Planning for Everyone.* London: Helen Sanderson Associates.

Chapter 16

Challenging behaviour and mental health problems

Sarah Halls and Saadia Arshad

Challenging behaviour is overrepresented in people with learning disabilities, ranging from minor antisocial behaviours to seriously aggressive outbursts. It is important to remember that people with learning disabilities do not constitute a uniform group; therefore it is unfair to gather them under one label or to treat them with identical interventions. It is also important to note that people with learning disabilities who present with behaviours described as challenging are often marginalised, stigmatised, disempowered and excluded from mainstream society; hence they can experience disadvantage and discrimination.

Defining challenging behaviour

Challenging behaviour can take many different forms, examples include:

- verbal aggression
- shouting, screaming and general noisiness
- physical aggression
- self-injurious behaviour
- stereotypy
- inappropriate social behaviours
- social withdrawal
- hyperactivity
- disruptive behaviour
- repetitive communication disturbances

- anxiety, fearfulness
- faecal smearing
- stealing
- destructiveness.

Prevalence of challenging behaviour and methodological issues

Prevalence estimates for challenging behaviour in people who had been administratively defined as having learning disabilities is 5.7% (Emerson & Bromley, 1995). Males are more likely to engage in behaviour described as challenging and the overall prevalence of challenging behaviour increases during childhood, peaks in early adulthood and then declines. The prevalence of aggression and self-injurious behaviour is greater in people with higher support needs. There are also certain methodological issues that need to be considered with regard to the prevalence of challenging behaviour. This is because the terms 'challenging behaviour' and 'mental health problems' are used interchangeably in some studies, thus questioning the accuracy of prevalence figures and making it more difficult to explore the relationship between challenging behaviour and mental health problems.

Physical health problems and genetic syndromes

It is crucial that the cause of challenging behaviour is determined so that effective interventions can be provided. There are many different causes of challenging behaviour and when someone is engaging in such behaviour it is important to rule out any physical health problems that may be causing it or are associated with it.

Physical health problems that may present as challenging behaviour include:

- Genetic syndromes
  - Prader-Willi syndrome: a complex genetic disorder, which is present from birth. Its main characteristics are excessive appetite, low muscle tone, emotional instability, immature physical development

and learning disabilities (sometimes very mild) (The Prader-Willi Syndrome Association, 2011)

  - Lesch Nyhan syndrome: a rare inherited genetic disorder that is present at birth and generally only occurs in males. This disorder involves a lack of the enzyme HPRT, which leads to the overproduction of uric acid. This causes severe gout, learning disabilities, poor muscle control, kidney stones and self-injurious behaviour.
- Sensory impairment
  - Visual impairment
  - Hearing loss
- Neurological disorders
  - Dementia: '*Symptoms that occur when the brain is affected by specific diseases and conditions. Symptoms of dementia include loss of memory, confusion and problems with speech and understanding*' (Alzheimer's Society, 2011).
  - Delirium: a condition of rapid changes in the brain and severe confusion; symptoms include poor concentration, poor short-term memory, delusions, hallucinations, incoherent speech, altered sleep patterns, emotional or personality changes, agitation, restlessness, hyperactivity, lethargy and disrupted attention.
  - Epilepsy: recurrent seizures that are caused by a sudden burst of excess electrical activity in the brain. This causes a temporary disruption in the normal message passing between brain cells and results in the brain's messages becoming halted or mixed up (Epilepsy Action, 2010).
- Pain and discomfort
  - Dysmenorrhoea (period pain)
  - Dental pain
  - Constipation
- Physical disorders including hypothyroidism (under-functioning thyroid)
- Infections: urinary tract infection (UTI) or chest infections may predispose people to confusion and challenging behaviour
- Side effects of medication including anticholinergic medication (such as procyclidine) and antiepileptic medication.

People with learning disabilities are more likely to suffer from physical health problems than the wider population, for example people who have

Down's syndrome are more likely to suffer from hypothyroidism. People with learning disabilities are also more likely to be on medication, which can have side effects. For example:

- anticholinergic medication (which is used to treat a variety of conditions including asthma, gastrointestinal problems, motion sickness and muscular spasms) can cause side effects such as constipation and confusion, especially in older people
- antiepileptic medication (used to treat epilepsy) can cause behavioural changes and can even predispose people to developing mental health problems, such as depression.

When supporting people with learning disabilities who have been prescribed medication, it is important that support staff are aware that medications can have significant side effects and that they are aware of and monitoring signs of these. It is also important that support staff are aware what the medication has been prescribed for, as some medication can be prescribed for different conditions.

Given the above factors, it is especially important to rule out physical health problems in people with learning disabilities whose behaviour is described as challenging. Support workers should also be aware of the signs of physical health problems in people with learning disabilities as they may not be able to communicate their symptoms.

Mental health problems

'Mental health can be conceptualised as a state of well-being in which the individual realises his or her own abilities, can cope with the normal stresses of life, can work productively and fruitfully, and is able to make a contribution to his or her community. In this positive sense, mental health is the foundation for well-being and effective functioning for an individual and for a community. This core concept of mental health is consistent with its wide and varied interpretation across cultures.' (Herman *et al,* 2005)

In the same way we can experience problems with our physical health, we can also suffer from mental health problems. Mental health problems affect one in four people in the world at some point in their life (World Health Organization, 2001).

People with learning disabilities are more at risk of developing mental health problems because they are more vulnerable to the factors that can predispose people to developing them.

Mental health problems and challenging behaviour

The terms 'challenging behaviour' and 'mental health problems' are often used interchangeably, which can cause some confusion with regard to the difference between them. Despite this, there are distinct differences between challenging behaviour and mental health problems.

- Challenging behaviour only refers to the behaviour and the effect of the behaviour.
- Challenging behaviour may be directed towards the individual and/or towards others and is said to have an underlying function, for example communicating the individual's needs or distress.
- The diagnosis of mental health problems relies on the presence of certain symptoms and signs, which have to be present for a minimum period of time and impair an individual's functioning. The symptoms and signs may include behavioural challenges, or may be characterised by specific signs, which will be discussed later in the chapter.
- Behaviour associated with mental health problems may not actually have a function and may just be a manifestation of the illness.

Despite these differences, it can be difficult to establish the presence of mental health problems and their relationship with challenging behaviour in people with learning disabilities. Challenging behaviour can be unrelated to mental health problems or it may be a manifestation of a mental health problem.

The relationship between challenging behaviour, mental health problems and developmental conditions is complex. Mental health problems may present with a number of signs and symptoms, which may also include challenging behaviour, for example characterised by aggression or agitation, and directed at themself or others. However, there are a number of people with mental health problems whose behaviour is not described as challenging, and likewise there are individuals whose behaviour is described as challenging who do not have mental health problems.

It is important for support workers to remember that challenging behaviour is more common in people with higher support needs. This group of individuals may, by definition, have difficulty in communication and especially in describing their internal emotional experiences. Therefore, it may be difficult for them to communicate and express feelings of sadness, anxiety or thought disturbances.

Causes of mental health problems

Mental health problems are caused by a variety of factors, which can be divided into biological and psycho-social causes.

Biological

- Genetic: certain mental health problems may run in families and have a genetic basis, however the relationship is complex and not straightforward
- Physical health problems
- Medication: some medication used to treat physical or mental health problems can cause mental health problems, such as depression

Psychological

- Life events including bereavement (loss events) of family, support worker, friends
- Reaction to trauma, including abuse or loss
- Expressed emotions and externalised challenging behaviour of children and adults with learning disabilities
- Negative learning experiences
- Stigma

Environmental

- Changes in routines (especially for people with autism)
- Other changes: in family, support workers, at home, in other recreational activities
- Transitions

In many cases mental health problems will not be caused solely by one of the above causes, but more likely by a combination. Although these causes or vulnerability factors will apply to people in the wider population, people with learning disabilities are more likely to experience them and thus are more vulnerable to developing mental health problems.

Specific mental health problems

Psychosis

The defining aspect of psychosis is that the person's perception of reality is distorted. It is important to remember that these experiences are very real to the person.

Psychosis affects:

- thought: the person may experience delusions and these may result in changes in the content of the person's speech
- perception: the person may experience hallucinations, for example visual, auditory etc.
- behaviour may become 'disorganised'
- insight may become impaired.

People can experience psychosis in a number of conditions, including:

- schizophrenia
- severe depression
- dementia.

Schizophrenia

Broadly speaking, symptoms of schizophrenia are divided into positive symptoms and negative symptoms. The positive symptoms include delusions, thought disorder and hallucinations and tend to occur more commonly during acute episodes when people are at their most unwell. Negative symptoms include a degree of withdrawal, loss of motivation and loss of awareness about socially appropriate behaviour etc. They are less dramatic than the positive symptoms but tend to be more persistent and affect everyday functioning.

Schizophrenia is three times more common in people with learning disabilities than the general population (Turner, 1989). The diagnosis of schizophrenia largely depends on people being able to explain their unusual experiences and symptoms. Therefore, such diagnosis can be difficult to establish in people with higher support needs and/or communication difficulties.

Positive symptoms of schizophrenia

Delusions

Delusions are fixed but false beliefs that are held despite a lack of evidence or evidence to the contrary. They are not in keeping with the person's cultural, social and educational background.

There are many types of delusions, examples include:

- delusions of persecution (paranoid delusions): a belief that people are out to hurt them or out to get them
- delusions of grandiosity: a belief that they are of great importance or that they have special powers
- delusions of reference: a belief that external events refer to them, for example a programme on television is about them
- delusions of control: a belief that something external is controlling them
- nihilistic delusions: a belief that they have died or that the world has ended.

Thought disorder

In thought disorder, thought processes are disturbed and a person has illogical ideas. When speaking, they may go off on a tangent and digress from the subject that is being discussed. They will also talk at length without reaching any conclusion and invent their own words (neologisms). They may also experience 'thought block' or believe that thoughts are being inserted or withdrawn.

Hallucinations

Hallucinations are sensory experiences that occur without external stimulus.

Hallucinations can occur in all five senses:

- auditory (hearing): hearing voices when no one is present (the most common type of hallucination)
- visual (sight): seeing people/creatures when no one is present
- olfactory (smell): experiencing strange or unusual smells
- gustatory (taste): strange or unusual taste in mouth
- tactile (touch): unusual feelings of touch, for example things crawling over their body.

Negative symptoms of schizophrenia

- Preoccupation with the 'inner world'
- Lack of motivation and energy, affecting everyday functioning
- Loss of interest in relationships and activities
- Slow movements
- Reduced communication: verbal and non-verbal
- Self-neglect

Mood disorders

Mood disorders are characterised by abnormalities of mood; mood may be elevated (manic), depressed or it may fluctuate between the two. The different types of mood disorders include:

- depression, which can be mild, moderate, severe
- mania
- bipolar disorder (formally known as manic depression).

Mood disorders are easier to diagnose in people with learning disabilities than schizophrenia due to the biological and behavioural changes, even in people with higher support needs.

Depressive symptoms

The core symptoms of depression are low mood, loss of energy and loss of interest in pleasurable activities. More specifically, these symptoms include changes in mood, thought and attention.

- Mood:
  - pervasive low mood – most of the time, on most days
  - irritability
  - depressed affect.

- Thought:
  - negative view of self
  - negative view of the world
  - negative view of the future
  - morbid thoughts, which may be delusional
  - feelings of guilt
  - suicidal ideation or attempts.

- Other symptoms include:
  - loss of attention and concentration
  - loss of confidence and self-esteem
  - increased or decreased appetite
  - weight gain or weight loss
  - sleep disturbance
  - decreased activity levels.

Some people who suffer from severe depression may also have psychotic symptoms. Examples of psychotic symptoms that can occur in depression include:

- Depressive delusions:
  - delusions of guilt – a belief that they have done something wrong, such as committed a crime or acted irresponsibly
  - delusions of poverty – a belief that they are impoverished or deprived of material possessions

  - nihilistic delusions – a belief that they have died or that the world has ended.

- Hallucinations:
  - auditory – hearing derogatory voices
  - olfactory hallucinations – smelling rotten smells.

People with learning disabilities who are suffering from depression may find it difficult to communicate how they feel, so for those who support them it is important to be aware of the biological signs, such as changes in appetite, weight and sleep patterns.

Manic symptoms

Manic episodes tend to be shorter than depressive episodes and tend to start more abruptly. Manic symptoms include changes in:

- Mood:
  - elated, euphoric, high
  - irritable
  - labile – frequently changing mood

- Activity and energy:
  - increased
  - 'full of energy'

- Behaviour:
  - socially inappropriate behaviour
  - sexually inappropriate behaviour
  - risk-taking behaviour
  - impulsive behaviour (ie. not paying enough consideration to consequences)

- Thought:
  - increased self-esteem, self-confidence and self-importance
  - delusions of grandiose role and ability

- Speech:
  - pressure of speech – speaking in a fast and frenzied manner, difficult to interrupt
  - flight of ideas – a continuous flow of fast speech with rapidly changing focus

- Other manic symptoms include:
  - overactivity, restlessness and irritability
  - interfering with others, demanding
  - socially and sexually disinhibited behaviour
  - reduced need for sleep or rest, usually leading to exhaustion
  - neglect of needs
  - excessive involvement in pleasurable activities
  - over-optimistic ideation (for example, starting things and not finishing them)
  - appetite disturbance
  - socially inappropriate dressing or appearance

Bipolar disorder

Bipolar disorder is defined by extreme changes in mood, behaviour and energy. Classically, periods of prolonged depression alternate with periods of mania.

Bio-psycho-social interventions

Mental health problems can cause a lot of distress and have a serious impact on people's day-to-day life and this is no different for people with learning disabilities. It is important that a variety of interventions are developed with the main aim being to reduce any distress to the person with the mental health problem. Interventions should be multidisciplinary, involving a range of biological, psychological and social approaches that will help alleviate the symptoms of the mental health problem and improve the individual's quality of life. It is important that any intervention developed reduces the likelihood of the person suffering from a relapse and promotes social inclusion, which is of fundamental importance to people with learning disabilities.

Biological interventions

Biological interventions for mental health problems involve the use of medication. The types of medication used for mental health problems include:

- antipsychotics, for example haloperidol, olanzapine, risperidone, quetiapinne and aripipazole
- antidepressants, for example fluoxetine, sertraline and venlafaxine
- mood stabilisers, for example lithium, sodium valporate and carbamazepine.

When working with people with learning disabilities, it is important that support workers are aware of the name and dose of medication that individuals have been prescribed. It is also important that they are aware of the side effects of the medication, which can be found on the information sheet inside the medication's packaging. Information on specific medication can also be found on the internet in an easy to read format for support workers to go through with the people they support.

People with learning disabilities may require regular blood tests and may need to have their weight monitored if they are on particular medication. They may also need to attend regular appointments with their GP and/or psychiatrist; support workers may need to accompany individuals for these where necessary.

It is crucial that support workers are aware of why the person with learning disabilities has been prescribed the medication, as they can have several uses, and to be aware of the side effects and accurately monitor for these. It is also important for support workers who are working with people with learning disabilities to, wherever possible, (with the doctor/nurse) educate them about their medication.

Psychological interventions

There are a variety of psychological interventions available to help people with mental health problems, which can also be beneficial to people with learning disabilities and the wider population. Psychological interventions involve talking and developing ways of coping.

Some examples include:

- cognitive behavioural therapy

- counselling
- psychodynamic psychotherapy
- behavioural therapy
- desensitisation.

It may be necessary for support workers to support people with learning disabilities with any 'homework' they may be given, such as completing mood charts. People with learning disabilities may be upset following a session so it is important that support staff can recognise this and react in an empathetic manner.

Support workers should be mindful that people with learning disabilities are not obliged to share what they talk about in therapy with family, staff or carers. It is up to individuals what they choose to share and they should not be questioned or pressurised to talk about their therapy. People with learning disabilities will be informed at the beginning of therapy under what circumstances therapy remains confidential and under what circumstances confidentiality can be broken. The psychologist/therapist has a duty of care to inform relevant professionals of any risk issues.

Social interventions

Social interventions involve creating environments that promote mental health and recovery and reduce the likelihood of relapse. As with biological and psychological interventions, the fundamental aim of social interventions is to improve the individual's quality of life and develop social inclusion. Social interventions focus on areas such as daytime activities, housing, social networks, recreation and relationships. When providing support for people with learning disabilities to promote their mental health, the following may be useful:

- involving the individual in their care plan
- improving individual's social networks
- encouraging individuals to join groups and develop hobbies
- employment and/or meaningful daytime activities
- ensuring cultural needs are identified and met
- providing a stable home life

- helping the individual to feel safe
- improving individual's assertiveness skills
- improving individual's social skills
- improving individual's economic security/budgeting skills
- preparing the individual for certain life transitions
- providing aids and adaptations, if required
- building individual's self-esteem
- setting goals
- staff who are accepting and non judgmental
- giving advice on health promotion, such as diet and exercise
- promoting independent functioning
- help individual to manage money
- involving individual in organising and running a home
- develop individual's domestic skills
- help individual with personal care.

Conclusion

- Mental health problems can be very distressing and have a serious impact on a person's quality of life.
- It is important that assessments and interventions for mental health problems are multidisciplinary and adopt a bio/psycho/social approach.
- The relationship between challenging behaviour and mental health problems is complex and it can be difficult to differentiate between the two.
- It is essential that staff have an adequate knowledge and understanding of mental health problems and challenging behaviour, and are able to support people with learning disabilities effectively and competently.

References

Alzheimer's Society (2011) *What is Dementia?* [online]. Available at: http://alzheimers.org.uk/site/scripts/documents.php?categoryID=200360 (accessed 6 July 2011).

Emerson E & Bromley J (1995) The form and function of challenging behaviours. *Journal of Learning Disability Research* **39** (5) 388–398.

Epilepsy Action (2010) *What is Epilepsy?* [online]. Available at: http://www.epilepsy.org.uk/info/what-is-epilepsy (accessed 7 July 2011).

Herman H, Saxena S & Moodie R (2005) *Promoting Mental Health. Concepts, emerging evidence and practice.* Geneva: World Health Organization.

The Prader-Willi Syndrome Association (2011) Website [online]. Available at: www.pwsa.co.uk (accessed 7 July 2011).

Turner TH (1989) Schizophrenia and mental handicap: an historic review, with implications for further research. *Psychological Medicine* **19** 301–314.

World Health Organization (2001) *The World Health Report 2001. Mental Health: New understanding, new hope.* Geneva: World Health Organization.

Chapter 17

Challenging behaviour and offending

Eddie Chaplin and Jayne Henry

This chapter aims to offer a historical background that helps the reader to distinguish challenging behaviour from offending. It also examines what happens to people with learning disabilities who come into contact with the Criminal Justice System (CJS) and describes the CJS pathway with reference to safeguards and protection for people with learning disabilities.

A historical perspective

The debate about links between intelligence and offending has been going on for centuries. Early positivist research reported that criminality was brought about by low intelligence. This argument is still put forward today by some who believe that the high proportion of prisoners with below average intelligence is evidence for this. Longitudinal studies, such as that by West and Farrington (1973), found that even when psychosocial factors, such as social and economic deprivation, family and individual behavioural characteristics, are taken into account, the association between intelligence and offending remains. Despite this robust finding, it is not clear how this relates to the learning disability population where IQ alone is not the defining criteria.

The link between intelligence and offending was cemented in legislation for much of the 20th century; for example, mental health law contained phrases such as 'moral defectives', which by definition implied a 'criminal propensity'. Up until 40 years ago people with learning disabilities were often housed in large institutions or asylums, later known as hospitals. Historically, many people with learning disabilities were not charged with criminal offences and any behaviour that might pose a risk to the person or others was managed within the institution. This model gave no consideration as to whether the individual knew about the consequences of their actions or whether the act was wrong, but instead focused on what security was required to minimise any risk to the public. This may have meant transfer within the institution or between institutions for more serious cases. This meant that hospitals operated as gatekeepers to maintain order among those with learning disabilities who had perpetrated criminal acts and also acted as moral guardians to those with undesirable or antisocial behaviours, for example prostitution, public masturbation etc.

The closure of institutions has necessitated a change in how we view and manage offending within this group. With inclusion into society also comes opportunity to commit crime and the expectation that people with learning disabilities who offend are dealt with in the same way as other offenders, albeit with appropriate, supports, safeguards and with a view to diversion to health care where appropriate.

For many, the distinction between challenging behaviour and offending behaviour is unclear. See Table 17.1 for further details. One is a social structure (challenging behaviour) and the other is a legal structure (offending). In law, the central question is: can the person be held accountable for his or her actions? For a person to have committed an offence they must know the consequences of their actions (*mens rea*) and to have carried out the act (*actus reus*).

The problem arises when people labelled with challenging behaviour are thought to know the consequence of their actions. It is important to consider if there are factors occurring that control and reinforce the behaviour that the person finds difficult to control or is unable to manage. This might include mental illness, impulsive behaviour or automatisms (performing acts while not consciously aware, for example sleepwalking). These factors will be considered in determining the course of action, for example diversion. A prosecution cannot proceed when someone does not understand the consequences of an action.

Table 17.1: Challenging behaviour and offending

Challenging behaviour	Offending
■ Social explanation of behaviour ■ Term used across the learning disability spectrum and is greater in males and in institutions ■ Although there are definitions, it can be misused to describe behaviours that cannot be tolerated within individual situations or services ■ Usually applied to those who are not aware of the consequences of their actions	■ This is the law ■ When the law is broken an offence is said to have taken place ■ Capacity is required to offend ■ Covers behaviours defined in law ■ Not usually against self ■ More evidence of planning and/ or conscious choice ■ For a person to have committed an offence they must know of the consequences of their actions (*mens rea*) and to have carried out the act (*actus reus*)

Once an offence has been reported the decision to charge someone is down to the police. See Table 17.2. Once the evidence is gathered the police will pass it onto the Crown Prosecution Service (CPS), which makes a decision about whether to proceed with a prosecution or not.

The decision to report crime is often difficult. Lyall *et al* (1995) examined the reporting patterns of services and carers for people with learning disabilities to the police. This study reported that theft and criminal damage were rarely reported; less than 50% of the services who took part would report a serious assault, and only three out of 30 services would always report a sexual assault or indecent exposure, leaving serious offences unreported. From this we can see that often the decision to report can be influenced by individual tolerances, prejudices or moral viewpoints, whether the capacity to understand actions is present or not. Whatever the situation, it is not the remit of carers to act but to carry out their duties under the law.

Association between learning disability and offending

While it is recognised that learning disability is not a direct cause of offending, it can play a role in understanding the factors that may be associated with an increased risk of offending. For example, people with severe learning disabilities are rarely found in the CJS (Lindsay *et al,* 2002). With other groups there are problems with the variability of methods and definitions used within research into the rates of offending in people with learning disabilities. The use of different definitions, criteria and settings make it difficult to generalise beyond the specific group of people being studied. Also, when examining the offending rates for individuals with learning disabilities, it is important to be aware that there may be a number of factors that may artificially increase or decrease rates of offending, such as:

- the under-reporting of offending behaviour
- being more easily caught by police due to clumsy execution of an offence
- poor crime concealment
- non-reporting of offences because they feel it is not fair on the person.

Table 17.2: Perspectives of carers and police towards prosecution

Carers' perspectives	Police perspectives
■ Attitudes and beliefs about 'learning disability' – responsible/not responsible ■ Previous experience of the Criminal Justice System – not willing to prosecute or over zealous ■ Concerns about the effect on individual's relationship ■ Worried about being blamed on an individual, service or organisational level ■ Being seen as a failure ■ House or work policies ■ Support from employers ■ Personal beliefs whether to prosecute or not	■ They are already in a safe place ■ It is cruel to put them in prison ■ It's a waste of time – nothing will happen ■ They will be a poor witness ■ They will go to hospital anyway ■ This is not police work

The Criminal Justice System

Safeguards within the CJS

Traditionally, the majority of guidance on supporting mentally disordered offenders through the CJS has been directed at mental health populations. However, more recently people with learning disabilities have been included along with other mentally disordered offenders. In recent times there have been a number of key polices and documents such as the *Reed Report* (1992), the Police and Criminal Evidence Act (1984) (which outlines the requirement for appropriate adults for vulnerable adults and children) and the *Bradley Report* (2009), which have led the way for the introduction of safeguards for vulnerable groups. It is not only current processes that are the issue, but how the processes we have need to improve, for example the *Bradley Report* recognises the need for early detection, joined-up services and reduction in waiting times between the stages of the CJS and the transfer to health care where appropriate. Offenders with learning disabilities will normally require considerable support within the CJS; supports available include the 'appropriate adult' scheme. The appropriate adult scheme is a safeguard designed to ensure that the proper process is followed and the person with learning disabilities receives the necessary support during their formal interview with the police. The role of an 'appropriate adult' is usually taken by someone who has training, works in local services, and does not have a direct care relationship with the person.

Stages of the Criminal Justice System

Figure 17.1: Stages of the CJS

- Caution. Charge. Take no further action. Refers to CPS.

- Is it in the public's interest? Is there enough evidence to obtain a prosecution? If so, proceed to trial.

- Fitness to plead (trial of the facts). Case dismissed.
- Sentence, for example probation, ASBO, custodial, hospital, disposal.
- Not guilty.

Police

The legal process begins by deciding whether a criminal act has taken place when a crime is reported. The police have a number of options at their disposal when deciding whether a criminal act has occurred, these include administering a caution (for this to happen the individual has to admit guilt), charging and putting an individual forward for prosecution, taking no further action, and giving police bail. If the police decide that an offence has taken place, they may arrest the individual and the person then enters the Criminal Justice System. This stage raises a number of important issues that are unique to people with learning disabilities. If the police decide to arrest an individual and take them in to be interviewed, it is essential that the issue of learning disability is identified so the necessary safeguards can be put in place, such as the provision of an appropriate adult during interview.

The Crown Prosecution Service (CPS)

This is the second stage of the process. At the CPS stage, the two criteria that are used to determine whether or not to proceed with a prosecution are:

- is it in the public interest?
- is there a realistic chance of prosecution?

There are a number of issues that may arise in relation to this decision, for example if the victim has learning disabilities, and whether are they a reliable witness. The decision not to go ahead with prosecution can be disappointing for victims and staff, and it may also have negative consequences for the offender, for example they may perceive that their behaviour is not serious and can, therefore, continue with future incidents without repercussions.

Advantages of prosecution

- Proves (or disproves) that the person carried out the act
- May help the offender get the help and/or treatment they need ie. via probation service, social services, or mental health teams
- Protection of the public if the offender is dangerous
- A deterrent for the offender
- It is inline with inclusion in society

Problems with prosecution

- It is a stressful process for the offender (and the family and support staff)
- A lengthy procedure, with a lot of uncertainty
- Costs to public (police time, CPS, possibly legal costs for defence)
- Stigmatisation as offender – may lead to some services being withdrawn

Fitness to plead and stand trial

Once the decision has been taken about whether to proceed with a prosecution, it is not uncommon in cases involving offenders with learning disabilities to involve an assessment to establish whether the individual is fit to plead. This is usually carried out by a psychiatrist who will need to establish whether the individual:

- understands the charges against them
- understands the difference between a plea of guilty and not guilty
- able to instruct their solicitor and follow court proceedings.

The court

There are two courts for criminal cases; the magistrate's court for less serious offences and the crown court where there is trial by jury. To make it easier to give evidence there are special measures that can be used with those defined as 'vulnerable'. See Box 1. The court determines guilt and passes the sentence from a range of sentencing options available to the judge, for example:

- custodial
- probation
- Mental Health Act
- community orders.

Some sentences need to be achievable for the person to be able to comply with them; this is particularly true for offenders with learning disabilities, for example often there can be difficulties with community and probation orders, such as setting restrictions, appointments for monitoring or attendance at programmes need to be communicated carefully. There is a need to check whether the individual has the ability to understand what is required and the skills to execute common daily tasks, for example accessing public transport, being able to read appointment letters etc. Breach of the conditions for a probation order, for example, such as non-attendance of programmes and appointments may not be due to non-engagement but may be explained by factors related to impairments in functioning.

Box 17.1: Special measures

- **Screens to ensure that all witnesses cannot see the defendant in court.** Screens are placed around the witness box in the court so that the witness cannot see the defendant, and the defendant cannot see the witness while they are giving evidence. The screens are placed so that the judge or magistrate, prosecution and defense teams and the jury can see the witness giving their evidence.
- **Video-recorded evidence.** This allows an interview with the witness, which has been recorded before the trial, to be shown as the witness's main evidence during the trial ie. the witness does not have to report again what they have already said in their police interview, but they must still be available to be cross-examined if necessary.
- **Live TV links, allowing the witness to give evidence from outside the courtroom.** This allows a witness to give evidence via a TV link from another room in the court building or from another building altogether. Although the witness does not come into the courtroom, those present in court (including the defendant and possibly members of the public in the public gallery) will see the TV monitors of the witness giving evidence.
- **Clearing the public gallery of the court.** In some circumstances a witness may find it easier to give evidence when the public gallery is empty. In such circumstances all other people taking part in the trial, including the defendant and legal teams, would still be present.
- **Removal of wigs and gowns.** Some witnesses, for example very young children, may feel uncomfortable with the judiciary and lawyers wearing wigs and gowns, and in some circumstances they can be asked to remove these.
- **Aids to communication.** This allows a witness to use communication aids such as a symbol book or an alphabet board.
- **The use of an intermediary (a go-between) only for vulnerable witnesses.** An intermediary is someone who can help a vulnerable witness understand questions they are asked and who can then communicate the witness' responses, providing fuller, more coherent answers to the court. They can help witnesses at each stage of the criminal justice process.

Although there have been debates for centuries about the link between offending and intelligence, these debates do not generally refer to people with learning disabilities. There are a number of methodological issues that make it difficult to explore this further due to differences regarding the definition of a learning disability, the definition of criminal acts, and issues around the reporting and prosecution of adults with learning disabilities. Nevertheless, many support workers and professionals working within services for adults with learning disabilities will encounter challenging behaviour and are therefore likely to be faced with the decision about whether to report incidents to the police as a crime. In addition, they are likely to have to support individuals with learning disabilities as they move through the criminal justice system. Having some understanding of this process, the safeguards and the disposal options is useful and can often alleviate anxiety about the legal system. While there continues to be some reluctance in reporting offences carried out by people with learning disabilities, it is important to note that with the appropriate safeguards in place the aim is not to punish the individual, but to ensure a fair hearing and appropriate sentence, which rather than being 'cruel', is a fundamental human right within western society.

Conclusion

- Historically, low intelligence was seen as a cause of crime, which can be seen in early legislation relating to people with learning disabilities.
- Learning disability is not a direct cause of offending, however it can play a role in understanding the factors that may be associated with an increased risk of offending.
- For many, the distinction between challenging behaviour and offending behaviour is often unclear, with one being a social construct and the other a legal definition.
- People often find the decision to report criminal acts difficult for a number of reasons, for example loyalty to the person, no faith in the police, believing that nothing will happen, feeling that the behaviour is part of having learning disabilities. By acting as a gatekeeper, this breaches the person's fundamental right to be heard by a jury or to access further support following diversion from the Criminal Justice System.

References

Bradley Lord (2009) *Lord Bradley's Review of People with Mental Health Problems of Learning Disabilities in the Criminal Justice System (The Bradley Report).* London: Department of Health.

Lindsay WR, Smith AHW, Law J, Anderson A, Smith A, Overend T & Allan R (2002) A treatment unit for sex offenders and abusers with learning disability: characteristics of referrals and evaluation. *Journal of Applied Research in Learning Disability* **15** 166–174.

Lyall L, Holland A & Collins S (1995) Offending by adults with learning disabilities: identifying need in one health district. *Mental Health Research* **8** 99–109.

Reed Report (1992) *Report into Mentally Disordered Offenders and Others Who Require Similar Services* (CM2088). London: HMSO.

West DJ & Farrington DP (1973) *Who Becomes Delinquent?* London: Heinemann.

